LARGE PRINT
CROSSWORDS

LARGE PRINT
CROSSWORDS

ARCTURUS

ARCTURUS

This edition published in 2018 by Arcturus Publishing Limited
26/27 Bickels Yard, 151–153 Bermondsey Street,
London SE1 3HA

Copyright © Arcturus Holdings Limited
Puzzles copyright © Puzzle Press Ltd

ISBN: 978-1-78888-110-4
AD006386US

Printed in China

1

Across

1 Front of a manuscript leaf
6 Novi Sad residents
11 Busybody
12 Heavy water, for one
13 South African grassland
14 Inlay on some guitars
15 ___ Lane (Clark Kent co-worker)
17 N.Y.C. cultural institution
18 Springsteen's "Born in the ___"
20 Thus, in Turin
22 Certain student, for short
24 French candy
28 Spanish houses
30 Helmsley of hotels
31 Became an adult: 2 wds.
33 Batters' stats
34 Heavy, durable furniture wood
36 Hamilton's prov.
37 Trig. function
40 Substitute: abbr.
42 Gp.
44 Complete taxing work online?
47 Cook, as beans
48 Fencing move
49 Chess pieces
50 "Holy cow!"

Down

1 Bible edition, initially
2 Hydrocarbon suffix
3 Fall down, as in a heap
4 Brouhaha: hyph.
5 Eye-related
6 Trinity component
7 Adjudicator, questioner
8 "Little Caesar" role
9 Real estate ad abbr.
10 "I ___ Dark Stranger" (1946 movie): 2 wds.
16 Blubber
18 Homeland Security org.
19 Go paragliding, say
21 La lead-in
23 Shrub also called may
25 Meadowlark relative
26 "Bring It ___ It to Win It" (2007 movie starring Ashley Benson): 2 wds.
27 Big name in magazine publishing
29 Challenge, legally
32 Five, for some golf holes
35 Conrad ___, "Original Machines" singer
37 Ball field covering
38 Floating, perhaps
39 "Don't let your boss catch you watching this" initials
41 "Bah, humbug!"
43 Baseball great Young et al.
45 Big: abbr.
46 Suffix meaning "recipients of an action"

The grid top row is filled in: R E C T O | S E R B S

2

Across

1 Able to fly, usually
5 Material that is forced out
11 Affliction
12 Appreciates
13 Chips in
15 It may be shadowed
16 Emulates Eminem
17 Make good on
21 Found a new tenant for
22 English class topic
23 It may have a lead part
24 "___ & Order"
25 Anatomical sac
28 Milquetoasts
30 Arise
31 Great Lakes port
32 Cries of approval
34 Basic, essential
39 Burrowing rodent
40 Powerful sea flyer
41 Not flat: hyph.
42 Tennis doubles team, e.g.

Down

1 "Desperate Housewives" network
2 Indochinese language
3 Glass tempering agents
4 Enter again, as data
5 Apt anagram for vile
6 South American stork
7 Keeps away from
8 Director's shout
9 Drive's start
10 Chucklehead
14 Breather
16 Beret-wearing "What's Happening!" character
18 Chiromancy
19 Visibly shocked
20 Trees used to make archery bows
21 "Harry Potter" garb
26 Bring under control
27 Gas up?
28 "___ Only Just Begun"
29 Ready to wear, perhaps
33 During
34 Large, like a check
35 "Eeew!"
36 Negative connector
37 Baptist leader?
38 Called the shots

3

Across

1 Combat gear
6 Humidor item
11 "Dona Flor and Her Two Husbands" author Jorge
12 John Cougar's "___ So Good"
13 Former coins of India
14 Apple desktops
15 Syrian leader
17 Santa's shouts
18 Feel like a ___ in the machine
20 "The Faerie Queene" character
22 Bard's stage direction
24 "I ___ top of the world!": 2 wds.
27 "Goodfellas" actor
28 Crazy person, slangily
29 Hydroxyl compound
30 "Batman" butler
31 ___ Kea, Hawaiian peak
33 Drink dunked on Super Bowl-winning coaches, often
34 Rap group based in Southern Chicago
36 Cul-___, dead-end street: 2 wds.
38 "Chicago Hope" actress
40 Snaps
43 Nutmeg state school, briefly
44 Chicago's ___ Expressway
45 "Chinatown" screenwriter Robert
46 Harder to locate

Down

1 Jump provider, initially
2 L.B.J. follower
3 Persist despite hardship: 2 wds.
4 Sultana's chambers
5 "Semiramide" composer
6 Scold
7 Ending for titan or thor
8 Whole wheat wafer: 2 wds.
9 Early record label for Bobby Darin and the Beatles
10 Letters for distributing news to Web users
16 Cunning
18 Edible European mushroom: var.
19 Anoas and gaurs
21 Innocent
23 Arthur Ashe's alma mater, in short
25 Sanctioned, briefly
26 Central point
28 Horror movie genre, slangily
30 Hydrocarbon suffix
32 City near Venice
34 Overabundance
35 ___ Noir (hybrid red wine grape)
37 "O patria mia" singer
39 Basic cable channel
41 Ethyl or acetyl ender
42 Old geographical inits.

4

Across

1 Place of worship
7 French key
10 James Bond movie of 2008, "Quantum of ___"
11 Coughed up
12 Code word for "S"
13 "The Andy Griffith Show" lad
14 Coward
16 Prone to acne, say
19 "My Big Fat Greek Wedding" star Vardalos
20 Inched
22 Mixer with O.J., popularly
26 Chaos
27 Biology lab stain
28 Make petty comments
29 Construction girder: hyph.
30 Polite shorthand abbr.
32 Name in "Nine Stories"
33 NBC news program
37 Exploitative type
38 Marked with spots
42 Chest muscles, briefly
43 Ford of fashion
44 Biblical verb ending
45 Rest periods

Down

1 Authors Lewis and Forester, initially
2 ___ polloi
3 Cream ___
4 They go off with a bang at celebrations: hyph.
5 Brown shade
6 Come to know
7 Spanish cloak
8 53, to a Roman
9 Willa Cather co-biographer Leon

11 Destructive black-and-yellow insect: 2 wds.
15 Japanese-American group
16 "I Ain't Marching Anymore" singer
17 Persia, now
18 ___ Strauss & Co.
21 Immune response orchestrator: hyph.
23 Suffix for abnormalities
24 First name of the star of "Schindler's List"

25 "You've Got a Friend ___" ("Toy Story" tune): 2 wds.
31 Flip of a hit single: 2 wds.
33 Copy, briefly
34 At ___ time (prearranged): 2 wds.
35 Kind of support, shortly
36 Pinot ___ (dry red wine)
39 High ___
40 Cry of mock horror
41 Internet protocol, initially

5

Across

1 Marathon
5 Lemon ____
9 Junípero who founded Franciscan missions in California
10 Sirs' counterparts
12 "What an improvement!": 2 wds.
14 Longboat propeller
15 Ingrid's "Anastasia" costar
16 Laundry detergent brand
17 Alley org.
18 Olive ____
19 Lily in Lille
20 "Lord of the Rings" actor Sean
22 Pastoral poem
24 "____ Secret" Kylie Minogue song: 2 wds.
25 Ho Chi ____ City (former name for Saigon)
27 Excited to the point of disorientation
31 Family head
32 Suffix with appoint or assign
34 Browning's "before"
35 Response: abbr.
36 Metric system prefix
37 Own, to a Scot
38 Newspaper Clark Kent works at: 2 wds.
41 Actor Murphy of "Trading Places"
42 Perfect or past, e.g.
43 Six, in San Jose
44 "Beat it!"

Down

1 Detox centers, briefly
2 Biblical mountain
3 PC component
4 Pleasant to look at: 4 wds.
5 Preparation of ammonium carbonate and lavender: 2 wds.
6 Cheerios grain
7 Not long ago
8 Food Network chef
9 "It's hard to ____ Trane": 2 wds.
11 Married ladies of Spain: abbr.
13 Accept
21 "Am ____ trouble?": 2 wds.
23 "____ Hear a Waltz?" (Broadway musical): 2 wds.
25 Single-celled organisms
26 Private
28 "Star Trek" counselor Troi
29 Most free from moisture
30 Buttinsky
31 Miami-____, southeasternmost county on the U.S. mainland
33 Milk-carton abbreviation
39 52, in old Rome
40 N.R.C. predecessor

6

Across

1 Latin 101 verb
5 Atmospheres
10 Praying figure
11 Playground fixture
12 Former
13 Closet wood
14 Metallic element
15 Swiss river to the Rhine
17 Grocery franchise letters
18 "___ Got the World on a String"
19 ___-Bo (exercise system)
20 Japanese electronics giant, for short
21 Math class, for short
23 Put up, as a picture
25 Gradient
27 Table mountains
30 Chorus voice
32 World created by Jim Henson for the movie "The Dark Crystal"
33 Bodybuilder's pride, briefly
35 Sticky stuff
37 BP product
38 Hard-to-___ (rare)
39 Grandpa Simpson
40 Lao-___
41 Regarding
43 Not acquired
45 Captain Nemo's creator
46 Cut back
47 Curve shapes
48 Yemen's capital: var.

Down

1 Advent
2 Seafood from Casco Bay: 2 wds.
3 "Wheel of Fortune" request: 2 wds.
4 Fender guitar model, briefly
5 Really funny: 2 wds.
6 Small: suffix
7 Occupying the front passenger seat: 2 wds.
8 Observational saying
9 Ridge of ice on a glacier
10 Fiber ___ (telecommunications technology)
16 Pleased sound
22 Fin. adviser
24 Tennis barrier
26 Subjects of wills
28 One of the Four Corners states
29 Respectful greeting
31 Religious day: abbr.
33 Mojave plant
34 Elaine ___ ("Seinfeld" role)
36 Enlists again: hyph.
42 Hurricane dir.
44 "We Do Our Part" org.

7

Across

1 Level, in London
5 Broadway opening?: 2 wds.
11 "… a bug in ___": 2 wds.
12 Jimmy Stewart played one in "Rear Window"
13 Actress Diana
14 Prepares to transplant
15 Biblical mother of Jabal and Jubal
16 T-shirt label abbr.
17 Roger in "Nicholas Nickelby"
19 OPEC meas.
23 Takes it easy
26 Contents of some barrels
27 Make smaller, in a way
28 His real name was Arthur
30 Foreign dignitary
31 "Be sensible": 2 wds.
33 Internet guffaw
35 U2's "___ of Homecoming"
36 Age abbr.
38 Kansas city on the Neosho River
41 Third generation Japanese-American
44 Chemical ending
45 Scarpered: 2 wds.
46 Artificial bait
47 Small sheepdog, familiarly
48 Dagger

Down

1 Singular, to Caesar
2 Desertlike
3 Rio de Janeiro's ___ Mountain: 2 wds.
4 Brainiac
5 Pull or pluck off
6 D.C. gp.
7 Laid-back: 2 wds.
8 Antipoverty agcy. created by LBJ
9 Crackpot
10 Hospital sections, initially
18 Big boss, for short
20 Springsteen hit: 3 wds.
21 T'ang dynasty poet
22 At a snail's pace
23 Behind
24 Cogito-sum connector
25 Doofus: var.
29 Overhead photos
32 Harden
34 Janitor's supply
37 Broken, old-style
39 Harp's cousin
40 Hard direction
41 Grads-to-be, for short
42 "That's relaxing!"
43 SSW's reverse

8

Across

1 Computer programming language, initially
6 Flog ____ horse: 2 wds.
11 Chicago Bears coaching legend Mike
12 Fab, in showbiz lingo
13 Spot seller, for short: 2 wds.
14 Awaiting: 2 wds.
15 Senatorial affirmative
16 Country in Eur.
18 Erstwhile radio duo, ____ and Abner
19 F.I.C.A. benefit
20 Professor's helpers, initially
21 Ending for pay or gran
22 More than willing
24 "East of Eden" twin
25 "Over There" composer George M. ____
27 Split
28 "Star Wars" name
29 ____ Tavern ("The Simpsons" locale)
30 Raiding grp.
31 New age chant
32 Welsh mountain valley
35 College founded by Thomas Jefferson, initially
36 Clothing flaw
37 Suffix with mock
38 Winter warmer
40 Everything, to Caesar
42 Kindle material: hyph.
43 Table of contents page, often
44 Color anew
45 12-year-old, say

Down

1 Times to give gifts, briefly
2 Gofers
3 Having a serious expression: hyph.
4 Alibi guy
5 Cylinder used for winding a cable
6 Broadway's "____ Irish Rose"
7 Cheadle or King
8 Powdery deposit on a surface
9 In conflict with: 2 wds.
10 Idle
17 Ball of cotton
23 Midback muscle, for short
24 Drink on draft
25 "Canterbury Tales" author Geoffrey
26 Beat, in a way
27 Behave
29 2001, to Nero
31 Practice public speaking
33 Correspond
34 "…And–which is more–you'll be a Man, ____" (Kipling): 2 wds.
39 Prefix with acetylene
41 Copy cats?

9

Across

1 Internet
4 Bustle
7 Faint
10 Fed one's face
11 "Get ___!"
12 Old Tokyo
13 New Zealand nocturnal reptile
15 Hang loosely
16 Croce's "___ in a Bottle"
17 Place in store, as green fodder
19 Computer text code, initially
21 Long-legged bird
24 Extinguish
28 Clean
29 Sponsorship
30 Voting "no"
31 Caustic material
32 Japanese-American
34 Projecting corners of a building
37 Eatery
41 Bend
42 Husband of an adultress, historically
44 New beginning?
45 Baseball game honcho: abbr.
46 Mount over the hill
47 Long period
48 Last word of "America, the Beautiful"
49 Manage (a living)

Down

1 James ___, Scottish engineer
2 Needle holder
3 Grin from ear to ear
4 "Caught you!"
5 Nonstop
6 Baiza spender
7 Kosher ___
8 Hot star, e.g.
9 Engage in self-pity
14 Giving instruction
18 Don Quixote's Sancho Panza
20 Call
21 Lawyer's org.
22 Member of Mayflower's fleet
23 His "4" was retired
25 Turkish for "lord"
26 1/1000 of an inch
27 Greek letter after chi
29 Brewpub offering
31 Take, as a position
33 Anvil-shaped bone in the ear
34 Chaplin prop
35 Black-and-white treat
36 Clickable image
38 Jim-dandy: hyph.
39 ___ jacket
40 Border
43 Many an IRS employee

10

Across

1 Treble clef lines
6 First common carrier railroad: 3 wds.
11 Famed restaurateur Vincent
12 "Yond Cassius has ___ and hungry look": 2 wds.
13 Already in being: hyph.
15 Supermarket chain letters
16 Prefix with lingual or lateral
17 502, in Ancient Rome
18 Golfer Ernie, nicknamed "The Big Easy"
19 Suffix with event
20 Pro ___ (for now)
21 Blocks
23 Professional sportswriter and boxing expert Kevin
24 Coffee order
26 Some health professionals, initially
29 "Shining Through" writer Susan
33 Suffix with glob
34 19th Presidential initials
35 "___-Devil" (1989 Meryl Streep movie)
36 Little bird
37 Guidonian note
38 Prince, to a king
39 Hearty repasts: 2 wds.
42 Mea ___
43 Roman magistrate responsible for public buildings
44 "Sunset Boulevard" Tony winner George
45 Part of a religious title

Down

1 Saw
2 Use Betadine, e.g.
3 Chicken serving
4 Cold War monogram
5 Object that is permanently in place
6 So-called "royal herb"
7 Computer key that's usually next to the space bar
8 Must: 2 wds.
9 1973 Elton John hit
10 Promptly: 2 wds.
14 Quick-tempered
22 Asner and Bradley
23 "___ Man Answers" (1962 Bobby Darin song): 2 wds.
25 Red with embarrassment
26 Violent attempt to overthrow a government
27 Exclusive circle of people
28 Singer Clark
30 Go after violently
31 Spiny cactus
32 Japanese teacher
34 Aired a second time
40 Mo. whose birthstone is the diamond
41 Author LeShan

11

Across

1 Brit's service discharge
6 Apt rhyme for "stash"
11 Actor Vincent of "Alphabet City"
12 Having a lot to lose?
13 Eldest Griffin child in "Family Guy"
14 Fragrant rootstock used in perfumes
15 China's Sun Yat-___
16 "Sesame Street" Muppet
18 Mathematician who is the subject of the book "The Man Who Loved Only Numbers"
20 Cooler
23 Time still to come
25 Take it for a slide, outside
26 Accord
27 Cut drastically, as prices
28 "___ Ado About Nothing"
29 Mammals of the weasel family
30 "Unbelievable" band of 1991
31 Bizarre
32 ___ probability (near-certain): 2 wds.
34 "Mamma ___" (ABBA song)
37 Say "not guilty," for example
39 Hibernation holes
41 Assured
42 Acclamation
43 "Alas …"
44 Census ___

Down

1 Prestigious mil. awards
2 Fencer's blade
3 It's described by the dynamo theory: 2 wds.
4 ___ roll (doing well): 2 wds.
5 Completely devoid of water: hyph.
6 Masked creatures, briefly
7 Dugout shelter
8 Breakfast for some: 3 wds.
9 Chu-___ (legendary Confucian sage)
10 Some M.I.T. grads
17 Fishy eggs
19 Baby ___ (candy bar)
21 Roll-top, for one
22 Old English letters
23 Feel vexation
24 "One" on a one
25 Cast aspersions on
27 Frying pan
29 Partner of poivre
31 Australian Aboriginal's war club
33 Hammer's target
35 Wrath, in Latin hymns
36 Heavenly subj.?
37 Ltr. additions
38 Hawaii's Mauna ___
40 Code breakers' org.

12

Across

1 Roadside sign
4 Author Lewis et al., initially
7 Tree juice
10 Award bestowed by Queen Eliz.
11 Ear-related prefix
12 Six-pointers, for short
13 Wick holder: 2 wds.
15 "___ for Iceberg": 2 wds.
16 Feline with a Magic Bag: 3 wds.
18 Shoe specification
19 Publicity, casually
20 Glows
22 Birdlike
25 Aircraft accident investigators, initially
26 Greek 'Gray Sister' who shared an eye and a tooth with Deino and Pemphredo
27 Island in the Aegean
29 Anxiety
30 "Mogambo" first name
31 Dizzy's genre
32 Eternally
37 Comic strip cry
38 Shoreline problem
39 "Evita" role
40 "Cry ___ River": 2 wds.
41 "The Sound of Music" extra
42 Kid
43 School grouping in some states, initially
44 Gunpowder or Earl Grey

Down

1 Amusing act
2 "___ Baby" (song from "Hair")
3 Economic situation in which goods are scarce: 2 wds.
4 Cajoles
5 Mo.-end document
6 Actress Loren
7 Obstacle to progress: 2 wds.
8 Sarah McLachlan hit of 1998 (or, backwards, an opera)
9 "Hey you!"
14 Rest on top of: 2 wds.
17 Makes poisonous
20 Part of Q & A, briefly
21 "Respect for Acting" author Hagen
23 Sailors' assents: var.
24 Pessimist's word
28 Queen song: 2 wds.
29 Overseas
32 Indisputable item
33 Eight, in Spain
34 "___ Tú" (Mocedades hit)
35 Don Juan, e.g.
36 Central Sicilian province

13

Across

1 Broiler accessory

5 Antigone's cruel uncle

10 Game on horseback

11 Elvis Presley hit "In the ___"

12 Harry Potter's Hedwig, et al.

13 Sources of illumination

14 Boise native

16 Court ruling?

17 Early 20th-century poetry movement

22 Curb, with "in"

24 Bad fit?

25 Unpleasant sort, slangily

26 Dull

27 Baja bread

28 Wistful word

29 To-do lists

32 Highest

34 Close to the coast

36 Jump or dance around excitedly

40 Commotions

41 Florida fruit

42 Stir-fry pans

43 Binge

44 Leg joint

Down

1 Go bad

2 Potentially explosive state: 2 wds.

3 Uncomfortable: 3 wds.

4 "___.0" (Comedy Central webclip show)

5 Cabinet filler, perhaps

6 "Andy Capp" cartoonist Smythe

7 Ordinal suffix

8 "Master Melvin" of baseball

9 Rejections

11 Razzle-dazzle, shortly

15 "Old MacDonald" sound

18 Brass

19 Dinosaur

20 Summer ailment

21 Big Apple attraction, with "The"

23 ___ a secret: 2 wds.

25 Curative waters locale

26 Low in pitch

30 Funeral song

31 Chips, e.g.

33 "Siddhartha" author Hermann

35 Bird of prey

36 Trigonometry abbr.

37 Dada father

38 Dictionary abbr.

39 Binary digit

14

Across

1 Lobster eater's garb, for some reason
4 Not lamented or mourned for
10 Kind of newspaper page: hyph.
12 Without an owner: 2 wds.
13 Skeleton part, in Padua
14 Go for
15 Capital of Mozambique
17 Rocket stage
19 Derek and Jackson
22 In secret: 3 wds.
24 "Barely Lethal" studio, initially
25 Up to me: 3 wds.
27 Dr. ___
28 Be unhappy: 2 wds.
29 Either end of a wide grin
30 German women
31 "Relax, soldier!": 2 wds.
34 Bathing, probably: 3 wds.
39 Dies ___
40 Official
41 Bismarck's state: abbr., 2 wds.
42 Approve of
43 G.R.E. takers

Down

1 Sound of thunder
2 Res ___ loquitur (law)
3 Sprinkle with mud, etc.
4 Not able to be defeated
5 Classic Japanese drama
6 Go a-courting
7 Coldplay's "Viva la Vida" producer Brian
8 Zoologist's foot
9 Mao ___-tung
11 Soft and sticky
16 Irritate: 2 wds.
18 Soft drinks brand of Pennsylvania: hyph.
19 Uniform armbands
20 Tex. neighbor
21 Auction cry
22 French wave
23 "A Doll's House" wife
26 Inform: 2 wds.
32 Coal-rich German region
33 Comic cries
34 "___ job's worth doing...": 2 wds.
35 Silent assent
36 Supply with weapons
37 "Don't tell me any more!," initially
38 Defunct org. that included Syria, initially

15

Across

1 "___ big deal": 2 wds.
6 Flees
10 Bogotá babies
11 Pinch sharply: 2 wds.
12 In an attractive way
14 Group founded by Daryle Jenkins, initially
15 Big picture: abbr.
16 Certain painting
17 Admonish
19 Two-year degree type
20 "Because of You" singer
21 Ex-Yankee pitcher Hideki
23 Greek twenty prefix
25 Kind of rug
27 Took a horse
31 Actor Chaney, Jr.
32 Drive insane: 2 wds.
34 Currency exchange board, initially
35 Athenian vowel
36 Son of Gad (Genesis 46:16)
37 Equivalent
40 Tampa Bay Rays coach Baldelli
41 ___ Antoinette
42 ___'acte (break between two parts of a play)
43 Lend ___ (assist): 2 wds.

Down

1 Natural
2 Cone-shaped home
3 Irritable
4 Opposite of alt: Ger.
5 Bone: prefix
6 "Turandot" slave girl
7 Coolness and composure
8 Coconut-based rum
9 Panache
11 Eagles, Falcons and Ravens, e.g.
13 Safe from injury
18 French kings
22 River to the Rhine
24 Regained consciousness: 2 wds.
25 "What's your hurry?": 2 wds.
26 Enlist for military service
28 Golfer Mark
29 Samantha's "Bewitched" husband
30 Worked on, as a newspaper article
31 "Filthy" dough
33 Buddhist principle of causality
38 A.T.M. maker
39 Cry of disbelief

16

Across

1 "All hat ____ cattle" (pretentious): 2 wds.
6 File coating
11 Fashionable mushroom
12 Dogpatch denizen Hawkins
13 Enjoys the pool
14 Part of the leg
15 Like Alberta's tar sands: hyph.
17 Dive (for)
18 Amount owing
20 Grass grown for hay: hyph.
25 Eskimo boat
27 "A Confederacy of Dunces" author
28 Expenditure
30 Pleased as punch
31 Oscar winner Mercedes for "The Fisher King"
33 Harvey Bullock of "Gotham": 2 wds.
38 "Wheel of Fortune" host Pat
39 Comic strip about a girl in high school
40 Popular aquatic performer
41 ____ Martin (Bond film car)
42 Architect Saarinen
43 ____ way out (finds a solution): 2 wds.

Down

1 "I ____ over this…": 2 wds.
2 "____ get it": 2 wds.
3 What a chuck holds: 2 wds.
4 Sedative drug
5 Ashley of "Full House"
6 ____ Band, Bruce Springsteen's primary backers: 2 wds.
7 When doubled, a food fish
8 ____ chief (mag. boss): 2 wds.
9 Actress Diana
10 "Uh-huh"
16 A U.S. Dept.
18 Bill and Hillary Clinton, e.g.
19 Flightless ranch bird
21 Kennel
22 Barrier where people must pay to go further
23 Commercial suffix with Rock
24 Sidewalk denizen, informally
26 Asian sheep breed
29 Deborah's "The King and I" costar
32 Fitzgerald and others
33 Author Roald
34 California resort city
35 It might be dropped
36 Ones in Spain
37 Danish opera composer, August (1859–1939)
38 Flagstaff to Tucson dir.

17

Across

1 Suffix for photo
6 Big donors, initially
10 Embarrass
11 Encore telecast
13 "Goodbye, ___ Jean" (opening line of "Candle in the Wind")
14 "What ___" (Mindy McCready song): 3 wds.
15 Antlered animal
16 Brit. news network
18 "Hey, you!"
19 Stocking material
21 Plum's center
22 First main part of the Constitution: 2 wds.
24 Richard of "Chicago"
26 Marlin or Cardinal, e.g.
27 Lively Spanish dance for two
29 "Big Blue"
30 Imitator
34 Gun enthusiasts' org.
35 Dungeons & Dragons game co., initially
36 Over or on: prefix
37 U.S.-born Japanese
39 "The Seven Year Itch" actor Tom
41 Like "20 Questions" answers: 2 wds.
42 French toast
43 Like Jack Sprat's diet
44 Move with a splashing sound

Down

1 Swindler, slangily
2 Carlo Levi's "Christ Stopped at ___"
3 DEA figures: var.
4 Doctrine
5 Process in which the product of one thing is the stimulus of the next: 2 wds.
6 Gutenberg's invention: 2 wds.
7 J.J. Pershing's command in W.W. I
8 Undermine
9 More foamy
12 Nights, in Napoli
17 New Year, in Hanoi
20 Solid
23 Fill to excess
24 Archangel who appeared to Zacharias
25 In one group: 2 wds.
27 Like a fish
28 Forbiddances
31 Green half of the band Gnarls Barkley?
32 Impressive mark: 2 wds.
33 Prepared surface soil
38 Alfonso XIII's queen
40 ___-Mart (retail chain)

18

Across

1 Lichen component
5 Turkish V.I.P.s
9 It may be spared: 2 wds.
12 As expected
13 ___ & the Blowfish (rock band)
14 "Carmen Jones" song: "___ Love"
15 Kindled anew
17 Backstabber
18 Fix, as a fight
20 Harnessed together
22 Battery type: abbr.
24 Retirement community restriction: 2 wds.
27 PC support staffers, for short
29 ___ Tower
30 Muslim form of salutation
32 Get ahold of
33 Others, in Oaxaca
35 Thespian's rep: abbr.
36 Waitress on "Alice"
38 Conversational filler: 2 wds.
40 Lease figure
42 Descend, as from a train
45 Baltic Sea feeder
46 Glossy fabric
47 Outfielder Lee ___ 1959–71
48 Blind segment

Down

1 Part of N.C.A.A.: abbr.
2 Killer of J.F.K.
3 Actor who married Amal Alamuddin in 2014: 2 wds.
4 Commedia dell'___
5 Sum (up)
6 Protector: 2 wds.
7 Ski resort near Snowbird
8 Part of CBS: abbr.
10 Overly smooth
11 Pro Football Hall-of-Famer Sanders
16 Bout enders, in brief
18 Soaks, as flax
19 Police officer training school in Plainfield, initially
21 ___ out (manages)
23 Powwow
25 Downer
26 Rank above senior airman, initially
28 Hindu garment
31 Rock's Michelle and Cass
34 Ward of "CSI: NY"
36 E-mail header
37 Mother of Castor and Pollux
39 Isles
41 Three: It.
43 "Isn't ___ bit like you and me?" (Beatles lyric): 2 wds.
44 Big blast maker letters

19

Across

1 Goddess of hope
5 Nina of "An American in Paris"
9 Ho Chi ___
10 Lost one's cool: 2 wds.
12 Dying words from Caesar: 2 wds.
13 Busy
14 Make less dingy
16 Shield border
17 Exodus pharaoh
19 Role in Haydn's "The Creation"
21 Providing comfort or peace
25 Click in telegraphy
26 Item that coyotes can purchase via mail, apparently
27 Commercial suffix with Motor
28 Edge of a road
30 Former White House inits.
31 Greek high flier
33 Like ___ knife through butter: 2 wds.
36 Red dwarfs: 2 wds.
39 Séance figure
41 Big furniture retailer
42 King of Naples in "The Tempest"
43 Director Riefenstahl
44 "___ Excited" (Pointer Sisters hit): 2 wds.
45 Those things, to Antonio

Down

1 Duck variety
2 Core
3 Whole
4 "___ Final Door" (Truman Capote story): 2 wds.
5 Language of Benin and Togo
6 Indolent
7 Mil. head honcho
8 Campus site
10 Shooting magazine: 3 wds.
11 "Do the Right Thing" actress Ruby
15 Medicine that induces vomiting
18 Fragrant compounds
19 One of eight Eng. kings
20 ___ Veneto
22 Abandons
23 Einstein's birthplace
24 PC linkup
29 Protests: hyph.
32 Of service
33 Simon and Garfunkel's "I ___ Rock": 2 wds.
34 Prefix with copter
35 Former Major League Baseball pitcher, John "Blue Moon" ___
37 Actress Sofer of soaps
38 "Je ne ___ quoi"
40 "Something for the Boys" org.

20

Across

1 Full range
6 "Do I ___ to eat a peach?": T.S. Eliot
10 Less than 90 degrees, as an angle
11 Grande ___ (La Sorbonne, e.g.)
13 "Chill!"
14 Utah's ___ Canyon
15 Oscilloscope part, initially
16 Drs.' group
18 Feel fluish
19 Japanese sash
20 Dil Pickles's dad on "Rugrats"
21 The Mormon Church, in initials
22 Boy, to his madre
24 Pituitary hormone, initially
26 Math subj.
28 Prince, e.g.
30 Peter, for one
32 Non-profit, voluntary citizens' groups, initially
34 Kind of particle
36 The Chesapeake, e.g.
38 Ad ___
39 "Hold On Tight" band, to fans
40 "Son ___ gun!": 2 wds.
41 Like one in a series
42 "Book 'em, ___!" (Hawaii Five-O catchphrase)
44 Overcome utterly
46 Several Russian tsars
47 Leisurely stroll
48 Part of a C.S.A. signature: 2 wds.
49 Networks: abbr.

Down

1 French waiter
2 Biting
3 Involving several countries
4 Hagen of "Reversal of Fortune"
5 State, capital Austin
6 Corrupt
7 Not down: abbr.
8 Regal title: 2 wds.
9 Charlton Heston title role: 2 wds.
12 Congers
17 Underground letters
23 They protect QBs
25 Midmorning
27 Freight unit
29 Rhizoid
31 W.W. II inits.
33 Dummies
34 Prefix with cab
35 Drudge
37 Talks foolishly or noisily
43 Weather vane dir., sometimes
45 Fodder

21

Across

1 Agency responsible for highways, initially
5 Snare drum noise: hyph.
11 Comb. form denoting flow
12 Bring to a boil?
13 Anthropologist Fossey
14 Elephant, e.g.
15 Having no name
17 Catcall
18 Snaky swimmers
22 Bowler, for one
24 Not getting up: 2 wds.
26 Like ghost stories
28 Plant pores
29 Geometric pattern repeated at every scale
31 Dress (with "up" or "out")
32 Font contents
33 Lunch spot
35 With very little space between: hyph.
39 Historical account or biography
42 Carve in stone
43 Come about
44 Calamitous
45 Showing gentleness
46 Pond gunk

Down

1 Pakistani tongue
2 Front part of the leg
3 Structure that is very unsafe
4 "___ Kröger" (novella by Thomas Mann)
5 Investment option
6 "Dinner at the Homesick Restaurant" novelist Tyler
7 Poseidon's weapon
8 Scottish hat
9 Certain foreign dignitary
10 ___ Avivian
16 Available, in a way: 2 wds.
19 Self-centred
20 Big car for a celeb
21 Grab
22 Bulk
23 Ethereal
25 The British ___ (Great Britain, Ireland, etc.)
27 Ready to drink, like a beer: hyph.
30 Worshiper
34 English university city
36 Not pre-recorded, as a concert
37 Off-white shade
38 Opponents
39 Assembled
40 The night before
41 Back-to-work time: abbr.

22

Across

1 Daytime TV offering
5 Does a trucker's work
10 Wickerwork specialist
11 Tattered Tom's creator
12 Oldsmobile model
13 Play parts
14 Islamabad inhabitants
16 Observers
17 Botanist Gray et al.
20 Himalayan cedar tree
24 Loser to D.D.E.
25 Grp. founded in Bogotá
26 Giving relief
30 Chuck alternative
31 Looks like
33 In pairs: 4 wds.
38 Commandment verb
39 Holy ___ Empire
40 Late, in Spain
41 Scintilla
42 Pied ___
43 Psychiatrist's appt.

Down

1 Large front room in a Spanish house
2 Short footrace, maybe: 2 wds.
3 Lofty perches
4 Tedious in speech
5 Zimbabwe's capital
6 Actress Daniella of "Animal Kingdom"
7 Rough-skinned tangelo
8 Some jeans
9 Fourth-yr. folks
10 Tube top
15 Spread, as hay
17 Dental org.
18 Caribbean or Caspian
19 Foolish creature in fables
21 Cry from Homer Simpson
22 Roadside rescuers, initially
23 Automatic update from a favorite website, initially
27 Tristan's love
28 Less of a mess
29 Obtain
30 Service station feature, briefly: hyph.
32 Trading places
33 Bangkok cuisine
34 "Star Trek" speed
35 "___ corny as Kansas…": 2 wds.
36 Apple computers
37 Fiji to Samoa dir.
38 Fuel additive letters

23

Across

1 "The Mary Tyler Moore Show" spinoff
6 Russian pop duo
10 Canvas supporter
11 Ken and Lena
13 Song on "Beatles for Sale": 2 wds.
15 Ceremony words: 2 wds.
16 It's like -like
17 Express regret
18 "Sisters" costar: 2 wds.
20 "___: Deadliest Roads" (reality TV series)
21 Criteria: abbr.
22 Raises a glass to
24 "Battling Bella" of 1970s politics
26 Abbr. in a letter salutation before multiple surnames
29 Butts
33 Actress Gardner
34 Pastoral poem
36 "Sure," slangily
37 Sounds of doubt
38 Tampa to Jacksonville dir.
39 It may give you more sleep: 2 wds.
42 To the point
43 From head ___ (completely): 2 wds.
44 Brit. decorations
45 Go too fast

Down

1 Pays
2 "You know how ___ can be" (Beatles line): 2 wds.
3 1970s teen idol Donny
4 In excelsis ___
5 Cool
6 "I ___ So" (Randy Travis song): 2 wds.
7 Muhammad ___ (boxing great)
8 River that flows through Baghdad
9 Not injured
12 Restores to copy
14 Philosopher Friedrich
19 Gray and Candler
23 Earthy prefix
25 Light winds
26 "That time of year thou ___ in me behold" (Shakespeare's Sonnet 73)
27 Made square
28 Matters of taste
30 Descended from the same male ancestor
31 ___ Tavern, Revolutionary War site in Massachusetts
32 Felt
35 Exams for future attys.
40 Bear, in Spain
41 Slice (off)

24

Across

1 Q trailers
4 Varnish ingredient
7 V-mail address, for short
8 Berlin wail
9 They put out blazes: abbr.
12 Brand with a spinnaker logo
14 Actor Stephen of "V for Vendetta"
15 Bk. of the Bible
16 Get the customer to spend more
18 Chef Lagasse who says "Pork fat rules!"
20 "My So-Called Life" actor Jared
21 Political cartoonist called "our best recruiting sergeant" by Lincoln
22 Muezzin's call to prayer
23 Certain noblewoman
26 "Dedicated to the ____ Love" (hit for The Mamas & the Papas): 2 wds.
27 No longer working: abbr.
28 "____ la Douce" (1963 film)
29 Short synopsis
32 Filbert
34 "Saving Private ____"
35 Suffix with arbor or app
36 European language
38 1950s political monogram
39 Punched-in-the-gut grunt
40 Class-conscious org.?
41 "Weekend Update" show, initially
42 Prime meridian std.

Down

1 Hindu queen: var.
2 Burst
3 French for "all together": 2 wds.
4 My ____, Vietnam
5 Adoption of customs, beliefs, etc.
6 Crack, in a way
9 Preserving by cooling rapidly: hyph.
10 Some river mouths
11 Beauty parlors
13 Spartacus, e.g.
17 Slovenly woman
19 Prefix with thermal
23 Expressed in speech
24 Bit of progress
25 Fiber knot
30 Checks out
31 Flip one's lid?
33 Roswell sightings: inits.
37 Patriot's org.

25

Across

1 New Test. book
4 Varieties: abbr.
7 Party planner, for short?
10 "What ___ going to do?": 2 wds.
11 Polish off, like pancakes
12 "E-Bow the Letter" band
13 Unblemished find for a book collector: 2 wds.
16 Name derived from the name of a person
17 Former New York Mets manager: 2 wds.
22 Horace, for one
23 Start of a French oath
24 "___ Can Cook"
25 Place of learning in Albuquerque, initially
26 Last in a series
29 Folk rocker ___ Curtis
31 Song from "The Little Mermaid": 3 wds.
33 "La Loge" artist
34 Sandwich bread choices: 2 wds.
39 Off-road goer, for short
40 Early role-playing game co., initially
41 Driving force
42 Ed.'s request
43 Lean-___ (camping structures)
44 Flushed

Down

1 Son of Noah
2 One of the big four record labels once, initially
3 Coal holder
4 Don't stop: 2 wds.
5 Carpentry grooves
6 Smarts
7 Butcher's best: 2 wds.
8 Fair-hiring agcy.
9 K-O connection
14 Bus. card data
15 Banks on the runway
17 "___ Believe?" 2015 movie starring Mira Sorvino: 2 wds.
18 Give ___ (care): 2 wds.
19 Hard hit baseball: 2 wds.
20 "Sesame Street" regular
21 Greek valley where games were held
27 Thousands, slangily
28 Newsman Peter
29 Cricket sounds
30 Prefix with nautical
32 Bit of statuary
34 ___ in king (spelling aid): 2 wds.
35 ___ loss: 2 wds.
36 Celtic sea god
37 Shirt size: abbr.
38 Put down new lawn

26

Across

1 Fries, often
5 Lennon's in-laws
9 Capital on the Bight of Benin
10 Pagan belief
12 Dependable sort: 2 wds.
14 "Trust in Me" singing snake
15 Part of an office sched.
16 Addis Ababa's land: abbr.
17 Small electric generator
19 Coastline feature
20 Blunted blade
21 Sounds some approval from a distance: 2 wds.
23 Steps over a fence
25 Buckle
28 Military sch.
32 iPhone program
33 Fatty, as tissue
35 Amount past due?
36 "Faith," "Hope," and "Charity" author Deighton
37 Longtime record label letters
38 Creeping shrub of eastern North America
41 Major can maker
42 Not separately: 2 wds.
43 Drudge
44 "Good Will Hunting" director Gus Van ____

Down

1 Sportscaster Dick
2 Big chill period: 2 wds.
3 "____ Day" (rap hit of 1993)
4 "Alice in Wonderland" tag line: 2 wds.
5 Self-inflicted disadvantage: 2 wds.
6 Actor Cage, informally
7 Yellow-brown pigments
8 Land of Robert Burns
9 "Don't ____" ("I don't know"): 2 wds.
11 Buddhist saint
13 Cancellation of civil rights, Bill of ____
18 Egg container
22 Big pile
24 Tetley tidbit: 2 wds.
25 Islamic decree
26 Mays' predecessors
27 English pantry
29 Lure: 2 wds.
30 Rise
31 Early American diplomat Silas
34 Actress Swenson et al.
39 Crag
40 Cape Town's home letters

27

Across

1 Titicaca, por ejemplo
5 Sum up, for short
10 Gross, in a way
11 Suffuse, as with color
13 Tubular structure in the body: 2 wds.
15 Capt.'s prediction
16 "In the Good Old Summertime" lyricist Shields
17 Prior to, poetically
18 Capital of New Hampshire
20 CNN correspondent Robertson
21 "Dangerous Angels" author Francesca ___ Block
22 Dump
23 Classic TV equine: 2 wds.
25 Charitable fraternity, initially
26 Feline line
27 Comprehend
28 Ending for second or sediment
29 Drop a hint
33 Record co. that bought Motown in 1988
34 U.K. honor
35 "Oy ___!"
36 High-speed transportation: 2 wds.
39 "1984" author
40 "Giant" author Ferber
41 "Fiddler on the Roof" matchmaker
42 Hammer end

Down

1 Mountain Community of the Tejon Pass, Calif.
2 Finnish architect Alvar ___
3 Complain
4 Bed-in for peace participant Yoko
5 Mexican muralist
6 Adjust, as text
7 "The Amazing Race" broadcaster
8 Hall of "Martial Law"
9 Immature and silly
12 Campaign poster plea
14 Automaton, briefly
19 Lower corner of a sail
22 Computer image file format
23 Planet near the Sun
24 Majestic pronoun: 2 wds.
25 Spawn, as offspring
26 Cuban dance
27 Understated
29 Make iron into steel
30 Circumvent
31 English Channel feeder
32 1979 Alda senatorial role
37 Football great Dawson
38 Agent, briefly

28

Across

1 "___ Freischütz" (Weber opera)

4 Dublin dance

7 Affairs

10 The ___ Glove ("As Seen on TV" mitt)

11 "I'll take that as ___": 2 wds.

12 It's found in banks

13 Open tract

14 Hwy. that begins in Astoria, NY

15 Suffix with effect

16 Difficult, laborious

18 College football ranking format: inits.

19 Abundantly

21 Mozart's No. 1 through No. 41, briefly

22 Cotton fabric with a shiny finish

23 Clad

25 Expire: 2 wds.

27 Ashcroft's predecessor

30 Final results of a manufacturing process: 2 wds.

32 Cut, as trees

33 Butcher's offering

34 Enzyme suffix

35 "Whom have ___ heaven but you?" Psalms 73:25: 2 wds.

36 Immigrant's class, briefly

37 Letters used (by some) for dates

38 Peck at

39 I-95, e.g.: abbr.

40 Pacifier

41 "Do Ya" rock grp.

42 Initials on old Asian maps

Down

1 Exercise in lanes: 2 wds.

2 Either singer of "Cathy's Clown"

3 Poker-table phrase: 4 wds.

4 Frilly neckpiece

5 Offensively prying

6 Travels a long way: 2 wds.

7 Some railroad cars: hyph.

8 Cassandra, e.g.

9 Generator element

17 Clear

20 Womb

24 Wind farm sight

25 Clinics, in short

26 Agency the U.S. rejoined in 2003

28 Los Alamos experiments, in headlines: 2 wds.

29 Stable worker

31 "Meat in the Middle!" dog treat brand

29

Across

1 Rocker Bob
6 City in Mercer County, Illinois
11 ___ orange
12 Cut into cubes
13 Method used for long print runs
15 Commonly: 2 wds.
16 "The Ballad of ___" Tennyson poem
17 Fix firmly: var.
19 Beginning stage of a study: 2 wds.
22 European fish
25 Of Europe, Asia, etc.
28 1960s campus grp.
29 In a rush
30 Slaver
32 Early stage of life
35 Breaks down, in a way
39 Alcoholic drink: 3 wds.
41 Frosted
42 End of ___: 2 wds.
43 Hodgepodges
44 One of 150 in the Bible

Down

1 Short-billed rail
2 Class for foreigners, for short
3 Cat, in Catalonia
4 Self-centered person
5 Grade at a gas station: abbr.
6 On ___ (how some pranks are performed): 2 wds.
7 Enraged
8 O.A.S. member: abbr.
9 Actress Laura of "Rambling Rose"
10 Greek theaters
14 Fabled outlaw: 2 wds.
18 "Kill Bill" tutor Pai ___
19 Compaq products, initially
20 Mortar porter
21 Reply to a ques.
22 "Is ___?": 2 wds.
23 "From ___ even to Beersheba": Judges
24 Taina of "Les Girls"
26 Letters that end "Old MacDonald Had a Farm"
27 "Ozzie and Harriet" family
30 Harsh Athenian lawgiver
31 Hall of Famer Sandberg et al.
32 Breakfast brand
33 Flour-grinding place
34 ___ B'rith
36 Highest draft rating: hyph.
37 Engage in logrolling
38 Get-rich-quick idea
40 Touch on the shoulder

30

Across

1 Blubber
5 Most wise
11 Palm tree berry touted for its health benefits
12 Blindness
13 Yellowstone Park sight: 2 wds.
15 Caterpillar hairs
16 Like paper clips
17 Rialto medley
20 Garden bloom, informally
23 Horse handler
27 Friend
28 Schiller's "An die Freude," e.g.
29 Turkish title
30 "One ___ Jump" (Count Basie)
32 "Hello, sailor!"
33 Grp. that awards the Spingarn Medal
35 Kind of drop
38 Chose
42 The study of birds
45 Bill with Hamilton on it, in slang
46 Barely beat
47 Stands for painters
48 Deep-six

Down

1 Captures
2 Crusader's kingdom
3 Delay action
4 Long-bodied reptile
5 "Erie Canal" mule
6 "Did you have ___ luck?"
7 Chunk of meat
8 Foil alternative
9 Chinese city on the Wei, old-style
10 Biting
14 #26 of 26
18 Hard Russian spirit
19 Avail
20 U.S. document publisher
21 Lake: Fr.
22 Cheer competitor
24 ___-di-dah
25 Conceit
26 Piano man Charles
28 Peruvian plant with edible tubers
31 Where much shopping is done
32 Small computer utility program
34 Make a dove's sound
35 Atom
36 Carpet computation
37 Bed & breakfasts
39 ___ list: hyph.
40 Breakfast choice
41 Changes color
43 ___ Aviv (Israeli city)
44 Many mins.

31

Across

1 Dried coconut meat
6 Willow
11 Brine-cured cheeses
12 Apartment that's owned, not leased
13 Made an emergency set-down: 2 wds.
15 It can be spent in Naypyidaw
16 Super-duper: hyph.
17 Becomes solid, like concrete
20 Nonetheless
22 Not just my or your
23 Put in order
27 Motion onward
29 Uncomfortable position: 2 wds.
30 11th of 12: abbr.
31 Smidgen
32 Go against
33 Lasting impression
36 It may be fragile
38 Mood lightener: 2 wds.
43 Combat zone
44 Not a soul: 2 wds.
45 Like stray dogs
46 Made level

Down

1 Ozone depleter, shortly
2 Above, in poems
3 Money-raising grp.
4 Scratches
5 Like an old grate
6 Spanish goose
7 Classical compositions
8 Prefix with European
9 Biblical garden site
10 Went on a boat or a plane
14 Church figure: 2 wds.
17 Jr., last year
18 Continental currency
19 Horse's gait
21 Formerly, in olden days
23 Community
24 Between eight and ten
25 Bobble
26 Deadly sin
28 Minimal wear item: hyph.
32 Sorrow
33 Ponzi scheme, e.g.
34 Mrs. Dithers in "Blondie"
35 "I'll second that"
37 Lady's man
39 Coral reef
40 Slip in a pot, initially
41 NYC to Boston dir.
42 Gave grub to

32

Across

1 Switch from paper to plastic, say
6 Fruit used in Caribbean cookery: var.
11 Teaser: abbr.
12 Brave
13 Gadget, slangily
14 Have ___ for (be perceptive to): 2 wds.
15 Awesome: 2 wds.
17 Business execs in charge of accounts, initially
19 Suffolk, for one, in Shakespeare
20 Former name of the cable network Versus, initially
21 Fixers
24 Campaign pro.
25 Prone
26 "Tru ___!"
27 Language of Stockholm
29 Brit. honor, initially
30 Carry
31 "The Hunger Games" fan, probably
32 Among other things: 2 wds.
35 Hopeless: 2 wds.
36 Circle
39 Castilian hero: 2 wds.
40 Gently and sweetly, in music
41 Composer Saint-___
42 Start of a clairvoyant's comment, perhaps: 3 wds.

Down

1 "Dark Souls", e.g.
2 Verdi's "___ tu"
3 Salad ingredient: 2 wds.
4 Tracers, bullets, etc.
5 Gunk
6 Plant with showy flowers
7 Don't believe it
8 Intelligent and well informed
9 "If all ___ fails…"
10 Close looker
16 Far from the surface of the ocean: hyph.
17 Officers, casually
18 Uninterrupted stream or discharge
21 Head waiters, for short: 2 wds.
22 "Streamers" playwright
23 "Nana" star Anna
28 Kills, slangily: 2 wds.
31 Early weather satellite, initially
32 Chemical suffixes
33 Italian city in Campania, Italy
34 City and commune in Lombardy, northern Italy
37 Rink surface
38 It may be high in the afternoon

33

Across

1 Fever
5 High-kicking dance of French origin
11 "___ want for Christmas …": 2 wds.
12 "How to Steal a Million" star Peter
13 Resourceful, enterprising
15 Famous advice from Horace Greeley: 2 wds.
16 Take out ___ in the paper (publicize): 2 wds.
17 Cry of a wild goose
19 "___ Not Gonna Take It"
23 Short coat
27 Where to see stars indoors
29 "The Jungle Book" boy
30 Lat., Rus., and Ukr., once
31 "Right Now (Na Na Na)" rapper
33 Bit of kindling
36 Pyle player Jim
41 1901 Kentucky Derby winner: 2 wds.
43 Annual showbiz awards
44 Cord fiber
45 Gift giver's command: 2 wds.
46 Proof of purchase: abbr.

Down

1 Former Defense Secretary Alexander
2 Red Muppet
3 "There oughta be ___ …": 2 wds.
4 Buster Brown's dog
5 Acrobat who adopts unusual postures
6 One day ___ time: 2 wds.
7 "Isn't anyone interested?": 2 wds.
8 Quarter, e.g.
9 Edison's middle name
10 Requirement
14 "Sort of" suffix
18 King Features competitor
19 Secretarial speed, for short
20 "Hold On Tight" group letters
21 Crude
22 Participate: 2 wds.
24 Hi-___, certain LP players
25 Belgium's continent: abbr.
26 Apt. ad info.
28 Animal on Michigan's flag
32 A Bobbsey twin
33 "The Cosby Show" boy
34 Chicken
35 "This ___" (Randy Travis album): 2 wds.
37 The Home Depot paint brand
38 A hundred bucks: 2 wds.
39 Dudley Do-Right's gp.
40 Aug. follower
42 "___ want a hula hoop…" (Chipmunks): 2 wds.

34

Across

1 "Norma Rae" director
5 Eye, at the Eiffel Tower
9 Agitated
11 Funny Youngman
12 College in Atherton, California
13 Mix with, as seasonings: 2 wds.
14 Greet at the door: 2 wds.
16 Suffix with Capri
17 ____ tai (drink)
19 "And the whole earth ____ one language" (Genesis 11:1): 2 wds.
21 Start of a Shakespeare title
23 Not invincible
26 Foot-long stick, often
28 Taj ____
29 Hide: 2 wds.
31 Element removed from gasoline
32 Joint appraiser
34 More: Sp.
35 Denver clock setting, initially
37 First part of a song, shortly
39 Brown ermine
41 First word of a counting rhyme
44 Kind of ray
45 Under, in Umbria
46 "____ Little Tenderness": 2 wds.
47 Item of footwear

Down

1 Mate for a ewe
2 "May ____ excused?": 2 wds.
3 Certain throat operation
4 Install terrazzo, e.g.
5 Brit. lexicon
6 Pressure time for many salespeople: 4 wds.
7 "What's ____ for me?": 2 wds.
8 "Fatal Attraction" director Adrian
10 Movie mogul Marcus
11 Two-wheeled cab for two
15 "____ the eggman..." (Beatles line): 2 wds.
17 Clay-sand mixture
18 To him in France: 2 wds.
20 Buccal
22 Ward of "Once and Again"
24 Laser-pointer battery, initially
25 Attys.' degrees
27 Ghost town in Custer County, Colorado
30 Skin blemish
33 Mail carriers have them: abbr.
35 N.C.O. rank
36 ____ chamber
38 Early models had eight-horsepower engines, initially
40 Dr.'s org.
42 "What Am ____ You?" (2004 Norah Jones single): 2 wds.
43 Nondiscriminating hirer in help wanted ads, initially

35

Across

1. Cat's place for petting
4. Good club?
7. Barker or Marley
10. Big shooter
11. Dance for one person: 2 wds.
13. Consider carefully
15. Hokkaido native
16. New Mexico's state flower
17. Sacred beetle of ancient Egypt
20. ____ Heyerdahl
21. Very dry, as wine
23. River to the North Sea
24. Part of the US–Mexico border: 2 wds.
27. P.I.
28. Gumbo thickener
29. Bread maker
31. Charge
35. Happen again
37. Fluish feeling
38. Likelihood
41. Heavy, waterproofed cotton cloth
42. Get prone
43. One-seventh of the rainbow
44. None has two
45. Boundary

Down

1. "Star Wars" director George
2. Before the appearance of life (geology)
3. Feather, zoologically
4. Animal that beats its chest
5. Video recorder, for short
6. Sports achievement award, initially
7. Stranded out of the water
8. Result
9. Makes dim, old-style
12. Hussy
14. ____ charger (engine performance enhancer)
18. Ben Affleck movie of 2012
19. Muslim woman's garment: var.
22. Cutting
24. Daydream
25. Chilled: hyph.
26. Port city in northeastern Brazil
27. Lethargy
30. Small protuberances
32. Nimble
33. Interrupt a conversation: 2 wds.
34. Atwitter, with "up"
36. Croupier's tool
39. Container
40. Plug-____ (computer patches)

36

Across

1 Decorative loop

6 "I haven't got it ___!": 2 wds.

10 Big name in astrology

11 Poet's "below"

13 Argentine dance

14 Organ-playing singer from Kaka'ako: 2 wds.

15 Tour organizer, for short

16 Start of the day

18 Danger in Afghanistan, initially

19 Round vegetable

20 Brief leaf?

21 Bettered "Better Homes and Gardens," say

23 Chest muscles, for short

24 I.R.S. employee: abbr.

25 Flier to Copenhagen, initially

26 Feudal underling

28 Bank info: abbr., 2 wds.

31 "Be on the lookout" message, initially

32 Letter from St. Paul: abbr.

33 Kind of battery, initially

34 Archaic term for one's father's mother

36 Black-throated ___ (Asian bird)

37 Clear

38 Handy

40 Bacteria discovered by Theodor Escherich: 2 wds.

41 Sunday singers

42 Massachusetts motto opener

43 Smallville family

Down

1 Baked entree: 2 wds.

2 Envisioned

3 Breakfast buffet choice: 2 wds.

4 Alternative to net

5 Walked heavily

6 Hindu god of war

7 Broadway brightener

8 Appearance in bodily form, as of a ghost

9 Italian, e.g.

12 Cletus and Boss of "The Dukes of Hazzard"

17 Ref. staple

22 Calendar abbr.

23 D.C. fundraiser

25 Fool, casually

26 American symbol

27 Make neat, smart, or trim

28 Shrinks' org.

29 Ace a test: 2 wds.

30 Horse operas

32 "Frasier" dog

35 Lagerlöf's "The Wonderful Adventures of ___"

39 Most common English word

37

Across

1 Like the "ng" sound
6 Boo-boo, to a tot
10 Sighed with delight
11 At right angles to the length of a plane
12 "Reversal of Fortune" star Jeremy
13 Publisher Henry and newsman Lester
14 Dream, in Paris
15 EZ Pass figure
16 Black billiard ball
18 Peyton Manning and Tom Brady, e.g.
21 Computer file container
23 Mary of "Where Eagles Dare"
24 First name in despotism
25 Also
27 ___ Lingus
28 Cariou of "Sweeney Todd"
29 Cub Scout leaders, in the U.K.
31 Not be up-to-date
32 East German secret police
33 Agile
35 Some G.I.s
38 ___ Delgada, E Azores
40 Every 24 hours
41 Lily family plants
42 "It's just ___ those things": 2 wds.
43 Bryn ___ College
44 Storage container

Down

1 "Precision Face & Upper Lip Kit" brand name
2 Bern's river
3 Kid's wintertime employment: 2 wds.
4 Virgil epic
5 The Mormon church, initially
6 Ancient Greek coin
7 Having the necessary expertise: hyph.
8 "Am ___ risk?": 2 wds.
9 Scrabble three-pointers
11 "Cat on ___ Tin Roof": 2 wds.
15 Hoarse, rasping
17 Affect, with "to"
19 Town north of Anaheim, California
20 Sun. talks?
21 Plug up
22 Concert sites
26 Semi-soft Canadian cheese
30 Owner of Menorca
32 Mrs.'s counterparts, in Mexico
34 Dino flyer's prefix
36 Blockhead
37 "Wynonna Earp" channel
38 One of TV's Ewings
39 Spanish wave
40 Medical practitioner, briefly

38

Across

1 Fond du ___, Wisconsin
4 Day ___
7 ___ water (it's from the faucet)
10 Adaptable
12 In the style of: 2 wds.
13 Jack, author of "On the Road"
14 ___-sequitur
15 Highest rank or level: hyph.
17 Express a point of view
19 Test, as ore
20 "Where the Wild Things ___"
21 Do poorly
22 Plant of the borage family: hyph.
28 Versailles to Paris dir.
29 Astonish
30 Lee or Levi's, for jeans
33 Photographer's request
35 Musical theme
37 The NHL's Senators, on scoreboards
38 Reflexive pronoun
41 Sea monster
42 Beat it
43 "Shoulda thought of that"
44 ___ Avivans (some Israelis)
45 "I approve"

Down

1 Albanian currency
2 Drink in a mug
3 Famed French jewelry company
4 Bonehead
5 "La Vie en Rose" singer
6 Enthusiastic approval
7 Flavors
8 Hello, in Waikiki
9 Undergarment
11 Any minute now
16 "Cast Away" setting
17 Blockhead
18 Ace
21 Gobbled up
23 Fellow, for short
24 Last in a series
25 Innocence: var.
26 Bird that's a pet for Harry Potter
27 Football kicking tool
30 Bank deposit?
31 Backward-looking, in fashion
32 Common aspiration
33 Baseball datum
34 "Gorillas in the ___"
36 First word of "The Raven"
39 Civil War general
40 Rx org.

39

Across

1 Desert fruit
5 Bother continuously
11 "Iliad" warrior
12 Practical
13 Italian "thing"
14 Bovary or Butterfly
15 Summer clock setting, initially
16 Lamb's pop
17 Line of seats, as in a theater
18 Large tapeworm
21 Jolt and bump along
23 Money guarantor, initially
27 Bridge abstention: 2 wds.
28 "Lemon Tree" singer Lopez
29 Art of speech, briefly
30 Sound the horn: 2 wds.
31 "___ Adventures in Wonderland"
33 N.F.L. linemen: abbr.
36 "Happy Days" diner
37 Defaces with rolls?: abbr.
40 In a spin
42 It's the law
43 Shrew
44 "God's Little ___" (E. Caldwell title)
45 "___ or Never" (Elvis hit): 2 wds.
46 Bypass

Down

1 Small river fish
2 Yankees third baseman, to fans: hyph.
3 Glass container in a lab: 2 wds.
4 Hockey's Tikkanen
5 Caring
6 "Me, too": 3 wds.
7 Embarrassed
8 Many miles off
9 Big league sport
10 Knocked off, in a way
16 In-basket stamp: abbr.
19 "Ring My Bell" singer Ward
20 "___ Man of Color" (mystery novel by Barbara Hambly): 2 wds.
21 Dad's namesake: abbr.
22 "___ la la!"
24 Rod for assessing oil level
25 ___ funk: 2 wds.
26 Op. ___
28 Gumshoes
30 Fill with air and swell outward
32 Florida's Key ___
33 Grammy winner Norah's Grammy-winning father
34 Blockhead
35 Wall St. units
38 ___-mutuel (form of betting)
39 Aerobic bit
41 "Sweet Tooth" author McEwan
42 Scale notes

40

Across

1 Rest day: abbr.
4 Set (against)
7 Add years to one's life
8 Plaster finishes
13 Levelheaded: 3 wds.
15 Musical composition
16 Alway's antonym
17 Chitchat
18 Port town on the coast of the Sea of Japan
19 Revised before printing
22 Russian fighter plane
23 Become less intense: 2 wds.
25 Prevent
27 It recounts Dido's suicide
29 General talk, hearsay
31 Matter in the Big Bang theory
33 Sch. whose song is "The Eyes of Texas"
34 Saffron-flavored dish made of rice with shellfish
36 Jay Leno rival: 2 wds.
38 Artsy one
39 Not, to a Scot
40 GBP alternative
41 Mdse.

Down

1 1978 Peace Nobelist
2 Ancient meeting places
3 Perplexity
4 Attention-getters
5 "Was ___ harsh?": 2 wds.
6 Mon. follower
9 "This ___ be!"
10 Sandwich cookie center: 2 wds.
11 "SNL" alumna Cheri
12 "Who knows?" gesture
14 Cell phone company
18 Eat to excess, shortly: 2 wds.
20 Rimsky-Korsakov's "The Tale of ___ Saltan"
21 A foot wide?
24 More magical or elflike
25 ___ Banner, secret identity of the Hulk
26 Cars
28 Remove element 82 from
30 Brilliantly colored fish
32 Long tresses
34 ___ and pans
35 Out for the night
37 Modern: Ger.

41

Across

1 Large number

5 Mississippi city, birthplace of Elvis Presley

11 Bogeyman

12 Dodger

13 Holler

14 Leave in a hurry: 2 wds.

15 Act like

16 1952 Winter Olympics city

17 ABC News reporter Potter

18 Frightened

22 Bunk

24 Hot stuff

25 Cashless deal

27 Southern lady's salutation, stereotypically

28 Caulking fiber

30 Interval

31 Of no value

33 Go with the flow, perhaps

36 "National Velvet" author Bagnold

37 Kind of deposit

38 Court contest

41 "It's so sad!"

42 Heathers

43 On or to the left prefix

44 To wit

45 Bit to split

Down

1 Martin's "Laugh-In" partner

2 Wide open

3 Donut, e.g.: 2 wds.

4 No. on a business card

5 Not windy

6 Palatal pendants

7 Complete view

8 Tokyo, once

9 Money in Moldova

10 Crumb

16 "How ___ Has the Banshee Cried" (Thomas Moore poem)

19 French bean variety

20 Stars and Stripes land, shortly

21 Break out

23 Plenty

25 Paltry amount

26 Is in the past?

29 Drudgery doer

30 Hallucinogen's initials

32 Spacek of "Carrie"

34 "Good job!"

35 Broom made of twigs

38 King's equal in blackjack

39 Hunk of history

40 Takeaway game

41 King preceder: 2 wds.

42

Across

1 Benjamin Netanyahu's nickname
5 90%, perhaps: 2 wds.
11 Mayan god of wine
12 Beaver or squirrel
13 Great admiration: 2 words
15 Ancient Greek galley
16 Male relative
21 Drink with a straw
24 Half a "Charlie and the Chocolate Factory" character
25 Desolate
26 Sales agts.
27 Sound
29 "____ of pottage" (what Esau sold his birthright for): 2 wds.
30 Cauliflower cousin
32 Film material
36 Complete disaster
40 Extent-wise: 2 wds.
41 Capital of Iran?
42 Prosodic foot
43 Goes off course

Down

1 Thai currency
2 Bakery employee
3 "Boss Lady" star Lynn
4 Not deriving from living matter
5 Fragrance
6 Oscar winner for "West Side Story"
7 Carders requests
8 O.T. book
9 Prefix with form or corn
10 Gas additive
14 Archaic past form of "be"
17 Hall of residence
18 Bob Hoskins role of 1991
19 Big and small, e.g.: abbr.
20 River of northwestern British Columbia
21 "Spare tire" stuff
22 Frown
23 "Novus ____ Seclorum" on a dollar
28 "The Plough and the Stars" playwright Seán
29 Yank or A, e.g.
31 Based on base eight
33 Island capital near Robert Louis Stevenson's burial site
34 Become friendlier
35 Adult grigs
36 "Le ____" five-act French tragicomedy by Pierre Corneille
37 Bibliophile's suffix
38 Middle O of O-O-O
39 Impressive skill

43

Across

1 U.S. Army medal
4 Relative of "Reverend"
7 1860s inits.
10 Tolkien cannibal
11 Number worn by Lionel Messi
12 Parrot's cry
13 Nicaragua monetary unit
15 "Vive le ___!"
16 Israeli oil port: var.
17 Trinidadian musician and bandleader Edmundo
18 "Cola Wars" side
21 Archeological site
23 River to the North Sea
24 Prefix meaning "one-billionth"
25 Know-it-all
29 Fund-raising grps.
30 "Dead Poets Society" director Peter
31 Seeming
33 Doesn't eat, for religious reasons
34 Hooded snake
35 Iago, notably
37 Golf peg
38 Fed juice to?
42 Swiss river
43 BBC rival
44 Devon river
45 Online feed, initially
46 "If I Ruled the World (Imagine That)" rapper
47 Coxcomb

Down

1 Wyatt's cohort
2 "No more seats," briefly
3 "Up Around the Bend" band, briefly
4 Popular vodka, briefly
5 "___: My Story": C&W autobiography
6 Caught: 3 wds.
7 Los ___, Spain
8 Faint
9 "___ Before Dying": 2 wds.
14 Abandons
18 Latin foot
19 Blight victim
20 "I Spent My Summer Vacation Rolling a 300" and such?
22 Napping, so to speak
24 Governed by Cuomo, initially
26 Cello elevator
27 Small bird
28 Fourth-year high school students: abbr.
31 Doha's land
32 "___ directed" (medicine alert): 2 wds.
33 Babes in the woods
36 Bit
39 Football official, for short
40 Outer: prefix
41 Passbook abbr.

44

Across

1 They guard sacks

8 Deface

11 Gate-crash

12 Buzz

13 Place for civil cases: 2 wds.

15 Hosts

16 "Here ____, there..." (kids' song lyric): 2 wds.

17 Brief shots?

18 Light ____ (insubstantial): 2 wds.

19 ____ Paulo (Brazilian city)

20 Expresses disapproval: hyph.

22 Pop-up breakfast fare

23 Anointing as part of a religious ceremony

26 Cut off

29 ____ bourguignon

30 Sagan of "Cosmos"

31 Sheryl Crow's "____ Wanna Do": 2 wds.

32 Extent-wise: 2 wds.

34 In silence

36 Ramat ____ (Israeli city)

37 District under the care of a bishop

38 Cyprinoid fish

39 Carpenter, at times

Down

1 They have pull

2 Inability to recall the names of everyday objects

3 Masonry finish applied when wet

4 Pelagic soarers

5 Quiet

6 "Grand" ice cream maker

7 IBM competitor

8 Terrorize or threaten: hyph.

9 Canny

10 Electric motor parts

14 Drying houses

18 Heaps and heaps: 2 wds.

20 Cry of relief, initially

21 Actor Tognazzi

22 iPod cases, in France

23 African river

24 Commission-free: hyph.

25 Singer Dion

26 Don who pitched the only perfect World Series game

27 "You won't like the alternative": 2 wds.

28 Cast member

30 Maine's ____ Bay

32 Nastase of the courts

33 Dodge model

35 Aug. hours in Akron

45

Across

1 Brick type
6 Mantric mutterings
9 Astronomer's sighting
11 Los Angeles street gang member
12 ___ table (dines): 2 wds.
13 Beauvais's department
14 Trendy berry
15 Crazy Horse, e.g.
17 Check
18 Sub finder
19 Composer of "Rule, Britannia"
20 Raids
21 Horton the Elephant creator
23 Certain fir
26 Some community bldgs.
30 Apple desktops
31 Sally in "Boston Legal"
32 As yet: 2 wds.
34 "___ Peach" (The Allman Brothers Band album): 2 wds.
35 "The Ghost and Mrs. ___"
36 Clear
38 "Girl With ___ Hat" (Vermeer): 2 wds.
39 Soccer score, sometimes: hyph.
40 Extra notes at the end of a letter, initially
41 Sol, e.g.: 2 wds.

Down

1 Cochise portrayer of 1950s TV, Michael ___
2 Frost remover: hyph.
3 Acquire
4 It has one's name and company information: 2 wds.
5 Italian note
6 Writer Fallaci
7 Lose
8 Catches, in a way
10 From ___ Z: 2 wds.
11 Ideas for interior decoration: 2 wds.
16 Mil. aides
20 Giant syllable
22 Atlantic Coast states, with "the"
23 JPEG alternative
24 Parisian passions
25 Women
27 It's "short and stout" in a children's song
28 Focal point
29 Gardener, at times
33 "Evil Woman" grp.
37 Verb suffix

46

Across

1 Wildebeests
5 When doubled, a Washington city
10 In ___ (hurried): 2 wds.
11 Grant-___ (government subsidy): 2 wds.
12 Hearsay: hyph.
14 Cosa ___, criminal org.
15 Fork over, with "up"
16 Original sinner
17 Army figure, for short
19 100 cts.
20 Skin: suffix
22 Principal dish of a meal
24 Having a sandy color
26 Minnesota iron ore range
28 "___ Ben Adhem" (Leigh Hunt poem)
31 F.A.A. airport service
32 Army rank, initially
34 Make a scene?
35 Chicago mayor ___ Emanuel
37 "Valse ___" (Sibelius orchestral piece)
39 Leech, e.g.
41 Loud-roaring animals of the cat family
42 As a result of: 2 wds.
43 Gulf of Aqaba port
44 Guesses, briefly

Down

1 Long, narrow depression
2 Place for young children: 2 wds.
3 DOT, alternatively
4 Having had the wool clipped off
5 "Buena Vista Social Club" director ___ Wenders
6 Relative of the buffalo
7 Hamper for dirty clothes: 2 wds.
8 Small
9 Stick
10 Bearded, as barley
13 Some "Nip/Tuck" procedures
18 Lennon's widow
21 ___ culpa
23 Air letters, once?
25 Weight abbr.
26 Monument material
27 And others: 2 wds.
29 Bands of eight
30 In ___ (like a baby, before birth)
33 Unrefined
36 "___ Lisa"
38 Critical hosp. areas, initially
40 "Spring ahead" hrs.

47

Across

1 Infected with bacteria
7 Agronomy concern
11 Italian cheese
12 Round buyer's phrase: 2 wds.
13 Ted of "Cheers" and "Curb Your Enthusiasm"
14 ___ cava
15 Abolishes: 3 wds.
17 Napkin holder
19 Yorkshire river
20 Letters in a classified ad. indicating a willingness to negotiate
21 Antares and Betelgeuse, e.g.: 2 wds.
25 Sea eagle
26 Some ranges, initially
27 Wallace of "E.T."
28 1963 Jack Kerouac novel: 2 wds.
30 Greetings
31 Nativity figures
33 Ethyl finish
34 Hardening of body tissue
38 Action at the office
39 Ready to be engaged: 2 wds.
42 Book after Proverbs: abbr.
43 Redecorate: 2 wds.
44 Encrusted
45 Florida beach town, familiarly: 2 wds.

Down

1 Low
2 What that is in Spain
3 Indoor ball game: hyph.
4 Zap with a stun gun
5 Patsy Cline's "___ Pieces": 3 wds.
6 Food, clothing, etc., intended for direct use
7 Cold War adjective
8 Lacking height or depth: hyph.
9 "___ Angel" (Mae West comedy): 2 wds.
10 Book part
16 Automatic updates from favorite websites, initially
17 Classical Library founder
18 Rock shelter at the base of a cliff
22 Glue, e.g.
23 Bit attachment
24 Mobutu ___ Seko
26 Gum used as a thickening agent
29 Rotten
32 Argumentative retort: 2 wds.
34 Design criterion, briefly
35 ___-Cola
36 Key's partner
37 Breakfast chain acronym
40 Not working any more: abbr.
41 Before, to a sonneteer

48

Across

1 Cynic's scoff: 2 wds.
5 1450, in Rome
9 Siberian port city
11 After, in Avignon
13 Religious building
14 Fire up
15 Govt. agency once headed by Steve Preston
16 Plow furrow
18 Org. for Heat, Hornets and Hawks
19 Stain removal product, initially
20 "Good ___ Been to You" (Dylan album): 2 wds.
21 ___ Nidre (Day of Atonement prayer)
22 Old magazine billed as "America's Aviation Weekly"
24 Apprehensive
26 International ___ (diplomat's area)
28 Lodge
30 Attire
33 Hospital sections, initially
34 Mets and Marlins div.
36 "___ wise guy, eh?": 2 wds.
37 "Forrest Gump" setting, familiarly
38 Baseball great Young et al.
39 R.V. hookup provider
40 "SNL" alum Cheri
42 Hand part
44 Kidney enzyme
45 "Kiss the Spider Woman" actress Braga
46 For men only
47 Furniture chain

Down

1 Lake ___, source of the Mississippi
2 Mishandle (a ball)
3 Shame felt when a guilt is made public
4 Literary inits.
5 Simone ___, Italian painter of "The Anunciation" (1333)
6 1970s sitcom "___ Sharkey"
7 Completely wasted: 4 wds.
8 Sappho's home
10 Actress Sedgwick
12 Simmons rival
17 As a rule
23 Frequently, in poetry
25 Part of a joule
27 Sport using the foil, épée, and sabre
28 Pay tribute to
29 Gives a speech
31 College pal
32 "___ Black Sheep" (kids' rhyme): 2 wds.
35 Ballpark figs.
41 Creek
43 ___ polloi (common people)

49

Across

1 Locale of William the Conqueror's tomb
5 One who eats no meat
11 161, in old times
12 Irish-themed Vegas casino that features a tattoo parlor owned by Mötley Crüe's Vince Neil
13 "E! News" co-host Sadler
14 Opera set in Cyprus
15 Gave a glare: 2 wds.
17 Boy, in Bogotá
18 Volume
22 It may be laid on thick
24 1993 Pulitzer-winning novelist Robert ____ Butler
25 "____ Carter" (Lil Wayne album)
26 Cause of some shaking, initially
27 English professor's deg.
29 "____ Future" (Alice Cooper song): 3 wds.
32 Unique person
33 Deanna ____, Marina Sirtis's "Star Trek" role
34 "WKRP in Cincinnati" actor Howard
38 Sky lights
41 Word repeated after "Que," in song
42 Like a bialy
43 1960s civil rights activist Brown, familiarly: 2 wds.
44 FedEx copy store, once
45 "____ forgive those who ...": 2 wds.

Down

1 350, in old Rome
2 Wings
3 Lessen the seriousness of
4 ____ acid
5 Kind of doll
6 "¿Cómo ____?"
7 Elvis Presley's "In the ____"
8 Alternative to shaving cream
9 Suffix with spat or spec
10 That, in Tijuana
16 Response card, e.g.
19 Elderly people: hyph.
20 Z-Ro album of 2011
21 First word of Massachusetts' motto
22 Battle site in 1944: 2 wds.
23 Dilute
28 ____ & the Medicine Show: 2 wds.
29 "And look you, here's your letter; this ____" (Shakespeare): 2 wds.
30 Horace's "____ Poetica"
31 TV series starring Brandy Norwood
35 Symphonic conductor Rapée
36 Get ____ deal: 2 wds.
37 Mane site
38 "All systems go": hyph.
39 Prefix with cycle
40 "Oysters ____ season": 2 wds.

50

Across

1 Earthlink competitor, initially
4 Some linemen, in football, initially
7 Passage
9 Metric measurements: abbr.
12 It'll cure anything
13 Sigh of release
14 Alternatives to plasma TVs
15 Daughter of Zeus
17 Crook's other name
19 Ink ingredient
20 Desire
21 Russian horseman
23 More soiled
25 Cultivated
27 Blvds.
30 Be
31 Modern letters: hyph.
33 Coined money
35 Four-time Pro Bowl tight end Crumpler
36 One-time domestic flight co.
37 A way the wind blows
39 Runway guess, for short
40 Madonna's daughter
41 Like 24 of the words in this puzzle: abbr.

Down

1 Amusing oneself: 2 wds.
2 Delphic medium
3 Airstrip: 2 wds.
4 U.S. Army medal
5 "____ Yellow Ribbon Round the Ole Oak Tree" (song): 2 wds.
6 The U.S. as seen from abroad
8 Rocket launcher, initially
9 Dish created by Mexican restaurateur Cardini: 2 wds.
10 Bouncing off the walls
11 Hit a golf ball wrong, sometimes
16 Engine attachment
18 Scarcely detectable amount
22 "Take Me Bak ____" (1972 Slade song)
24 Computer acronym
25 View for a further time
26 An exiled American, shortly
28 Big cat in Caen
29 Coasters
32 Bryn ____, college in Pennsylvania
34 Civil Rights Act grp.
38 Pol., Port., etc.

51

Across

1 Kind of wheel

7 Actor Hakeem ____-Kazim, Colonel Iké Dubaku in "24"

10 Go back

11 Darkens

12 Reduced, in a way: 2 wds.

13 Little bit of everything dish

14 Shared by all

16 Development area: 2 wds.

19 ____-Flush (former bathroom cleaner)

20 Made a shrill cry

24 "Over the moon," e.g.

26 Croatian leader?

27 Transgressed

29 Sculptor, painter and architect, ____ Lorenzo Bernini

30 Edge along some mountaintops

32 Early Christian church

35 One-time Tampa Bay Buccaneers tackle Jason

36 More snug

40 Together, musically: 2 wds.

41 "Ocean's ____"

42 "Kidnapped" monogram

43 Long arm of the Indian Ocean: 2 wds.

Down

1 Away, idiomatically

2 Velvet finish?

3 Candy striper's coworkers, shortly

4 Period between a stimulus and response: 2 wds.

5 Eskimo's house

6 Suitable

7 Baking locale

8 "____ Psycho" (song by Midwest rapper Tech N9ne): 3 wds.

9 Class for foreigners, for short

11 Having two layers of glass (windows): hyph.

15 Actress Marsh and others

16 Pitchfork-shaped letters

17 "____ but known…": 2 wds.

18 "Come ____!" (enter): 2 wds.

21 Toyota hybrid models

22 Abba of Israel

23 Janet Jackson's "What Have You ____ for Me Lately?"

25 European thrush

28 Windshield clearer: hyph.

31 Sorbonne, e.g.

32 Big pig

33 Extra: abbr.

34 Kind of chef

37 E.R. hookups

38 Wide shoe width

39 Biology letters

52

Across

1 Mus. chord: 2 wds.
5 Tastelessly showy in manner
11 Bring down
12 Charge: 2 wds.
13 "Look ____ Now, Mother!" (Gayle Kirschenbaum movie of 2015): 2 wds.
14 Deaden
15 Major road or highway
17 Bliss
22 Mustard family member
26 French girl, briefly
27 Non-reactive, like some gases
28 Entire range
29 "I Wish" rapper ____-Lo
30 My friend, in Marseilles: 2 wds.
31 Automobile safety device: 2 wds.
33 Accelerated a motor, casually
38 Movie of someone's life
42 Change
43 Cotton fabric
44 Cut short
45 Heart implants
46 Improve, as acting skills

Down

1 What the suspicious may smell: 2 wds.
2 S.A.T. section
3 Cote d'____
4 "____, Joy of Man's Desiring"
5 Bring up (as a topic)
6 Dee and Dandridge
7 Curaçao clock setting letters
8 Egyptian god of light and air
9 ____ Bernardino
10 Col. in a profit-and-loss statement
16 Left on the map
18 Bad bill collector?: hyph.
19 "Brokeback Mountain" heroine
20 Inner-city blight
21 Bigfoot's Asian cousin
22 Specialized computer, for short
23 "Diana" crooner
24 Tick's host, maybe
25 Fits of rage
28 Don't skip: 2 wds.
30 Imelda or Ferdinand
32 Expel a tenant
34 Gp. of musicians
35 Prefix with dramatic
36 Scottish capital, briefly
37 Blockhead
38 N.C.A.A. football ranking system
39 "Can ____ least sit down?": 2 wds.
40 "____ Buttermilk Sky" (Hoagy Carmichael song)
41 Jewelry box item

53

Across

1 Having a curved symmetrical structure
7 27, to 3
11 Beyond expectation: 2 wds.
12 Words before "instant" and "hour": 2 wds.
13 Dealer in rare books
15 Central parts
16 Nationals grp.
17 "Best wishes!"
20 Russian fighter
21 Harder to grasp
24 Spring source
27 Baby's soft shoe
28 Suffix with auction
29 Shrimps and lobsters
32 "Let me see…"
34 Chowder morsel
35 By necessity
40 Diva Horne
41 Checkers of vital signs
42 Poehler and Grant
43 Type of fuel distilled from petroleum: 2 wds.

Down

1 Dr.'s order?
2 Harry Potter's best friend
3 Kind of computer monitor, for short
4 Processed foods manufacturer
5 Ending for Kafka or Reagan
6 Duplicitous: hyph.
7 Fig. with a diameter
8 Neither welcome nor wanted
9 Jezebel's idol
10 Feminine suffix
14 In ___ (agitated): 2 wds.
17 Catalan surrealist
18 Large number: 3 wds.
19 Suffix for pay
20 Classic British sports car
22 Wide widths, initially
23 Grammar school basics, for short
25 Indian tribe for whom a state is named
26 ___ Wafers
30 "The Taming of the Shrew" city
31 Actor Epps and others
32 Hawaiian shake?
33 Memory: prefix
36 Tubular body structure
37 Musicians based in Maryland, initially
38 Island chain?
39 Maker of Touche Éclat, initially

54

Across

1 Kicked

7 Jeanne d'Arc, e.g.: abbr.

10 Old-fashioned

12 Money for waiting?

13 Become progressively worse

15 Drink holder

16 Sporty Chevy, briefly

17 Anglo-Saxon slave

18 Little flower leaves

19 Catch the idea

20 King of pop

21 Does some boo-hooing

22 Over the hill: 2 wds.

24 Welfare org.

27 Double bass cousins

28 Intestinal parts

29 Charged particle

30 Beauty shop

31 Person not living in a particular place

33 Run-of-the-mill: abbr.

34 Renew the outline of

35 That, in Chile

36 Political pundit Myers: 2 wds.

Down

1 Stars in many westerns

2 Ending words of a threat: 2 wds.

3 Gas number

4 The ones here

5 Canal sites

6 502, in Roman numerals

7 Relating to a nation

8 Jot

9 Olympic swords

11 Put a lid on

14 Deadbeats' cars, eventually: abbr.

18 Yachts have them

20 Bing Crosby, for one

21 Red or yellow

22 Barbershop quartet members

23 Brazilian beach resort

24 Remove all metallic traces from

25 Torch holder

26 River in South Carolina

27 Dugout, for one

28 Fighting force

30 Locale

32 But, to Nero

55

Across

1 "What ___?": 2 wds.
5 Brag
10 Copter's cousin
11 Rich tapestry
12 Hard and shrewd bargaining: 2 wds.
14 "All Things Considered" reporter Shapiro
15 Accident investigating org.
16 ___ de Cervantes, "Don Quixote" author
18 "Son of Frankenstein" blacksmith
22 Photographer Adams
24 Writer LeShan
25 Kind of nerve
27 More fitting
29 Sporty truck
30 Carpe ___ (seize all): Lat.
32 Use a stun gun
34 ___ Delacroix ("The Green Mile" protagonist)
37 Chi follower
39 Cast
40 Agent who conducts a sale by lots
43 Queen of ___ (Biblical character)
44 Nuclear fission co-discoverer Otto
45 "___ Pretty" (song from "West Side Story"): 2 wds.
46 Cholesterol varieties, initially

Down

1 Ancient British and Irish alphabet
2 Flowers, in Florence
3 Brings water to
4 Fros' mates
5 Fight
6 Bobby and Colton
7 Mecca's land, in poetry
8 Melancholy
9 Philosopher Lao-___
13 "Oedipe" composer Georges
17 Prefix meaning "one"
19 Makes progress: 2 wds.
20 Homage in verse
21 Computer file format, initially
23 Nautical shout: 2 wds.
25 Not at home
26 School grp.
28 More, in music
31 Kind of labor
33 One running the show
35 Mercedes of "Lost in Yonkers"
36 Father-and-daughter Hollywood duo
38 "Could ___ I'm Falling in Love" (The Spinners song): 2 wds.
40 Flt. gauge
41 "Weird Al" Yankovic movie
42 Chicago Blackhawks, Toronto Maple Leafs, etc.

56

Across

1 Auctioneer's responsibility, essentially
5 Ancient Greek coin
9 Medicinal plants
11 ___ Circus (old Vatican area)
13 Former 20-dollar coin: 2 wds.
15 Concealed
16 They're filled at the pharmacy, for short
17 "When We Were Kings" subject
18 Bring to bear
19 Attend as an observer: 3 wds.
21 Belgrade native
23 Latin American shawl: var.
24 Turf intro
26 Win over
29 Popular college guy, initially
33 "Siddhartha" author Hesse
35 One type of nest egg, briefly
36 Land in la mer
37 Company with a dog in its logo, initially
38 Popular wine, for short
39 Not large or small: hyph.
42 Fluid transition
43 Gland: prefix
44 Inf. unit
45 Foreword: abbr.

Down

1 Hindu holy men
2 Horror movie directed by Robert Legato
3 With more volume
4 Independent nat. since November 1941
5 Poor movie rating: 2 wds.
6 "___ sport": 2 wds.
7 Princess Leia ___
8 Move in an ungainly way
10 Some cameras, initially
12 Angler's gear
14 Being
20 Ethnic group of Ethiopia
22 Emerald City's creator
25 Red shade
26 Wedges
27 More slippery
28 Bring (up)
30 One of a ship's main masts
31 Get situated
32 Openness
34 "Apollo 13" org.
40 Grooved on
41 Former dictator ___ Amin

57

Across

1 Entrances for colliers
6 Part of some joints
11 "___ disturb": 2 wds.
12 Cowboy's rope
13 "The Wreck of the Mary ___"
14 Bury
15 "Boo-o-o!"
16 Veterinary anesthetic, initially
18 Risk assessors' group, initially
19 One of the friends on "Friends"
21 "Sophie's Choice" Oscar winner
24 Tatting outcome
27 "How Do I Live" singer Rimes
28 Climber's spike
29 Defeatist's word
30 Attacks
31 Mouths off
33 "Zip-A-Dee-Doo-___"
35 It fits in a lock
36 Geog. feature
39 "___ time" (Hemingway stories): 2 wds.
41 "Dallas" Miss
43 Signal carrier in the body
44 Renaissance painter Andrea del ___
45 Pollux, e.g.: 2 wds.
46 Dirks of yore

Down

1 Tacks on
2 Mother deer
3 Balin and Claire
4 Rocky hill
5 King who wrote "Cell"
6 Hogwash
7 Article in Augsburg
8 Sicken
9 Other, in Uruguay
10 "Peter Pan" dog
17 Officer
19 Five: prefix
20 Nirvana
21 Utah metropolis, initially
22 Drink with scones
23 Became depleted: 2 wds.
25 Rollaway
26 Printing measures
28 Noblewoman
30 Big inits. in camping
32 More miffed
33 Drop shot, in tennis
34 French donkeys
36 "___ pastore" (opera by Mozart): 2 wds.
37 Location
38 13 popes, so far
40 Sch. founded by Thomas Jefferson
42 Linked-computers acronym

58

Across

1 Animal with two feet
6 "Carmina Burana" composer Carl
10 Alpine feeder
11 Country great Haggard
13 Association
15 Comcast and NetZero, e.g.
16 P.T.A. interest, briefly
17 Shogun's capital
19 Dummy
21 Garden product word
22 Sound recording
25 French W.W. I soldier
26 Flat, simple boats
29 Large and important church
31 Final: abbr.
33 Appearance-challenged woman
34 "…all that wealth ___ gave": Gray
35 It's bought by the bar
37 Amble
39 They're awarded annually on December 10th: 2 wds.
43 "Duino Elegies" poet
44 Brain passages
45 Wide widths, initially
46 200 precious milligrams

Down

1 Pen or lighter brand
2 Bar opener?
3 Arrangement of chemical elements by atomic number: 2 wds.
4 Misdials, e.g.
5 Georgia, Alabama, Louisiana, etc.: 2 wds.
6 Grandma: Ger.
7 Network of blood vessels or nerves
8 Kitchen appliance: hyph.
9 Bread ingredient
12 Old ExxonMobil brand name
14 Aspiring atty.'s exam
17 Literary monogram
18 Electronic act Justice, e.g.
20 One-time widely-used pain reliever
23 Dockworkers' gp.
24 Walk softly
27 ___ kwon do
28 Camera inits.
30 Angelic instrument
31 Mil. backup group
32 He outranks the sarge
36 "Lion dog," briefly
38 Ars longa, ___ brevis
40 "___ Liaisons Dangereuses"
41 It's full of periods
42 Mach 1 breaker, initially

59

Across

1 Budding entrepreneurs, for short
5 Threads carried by weaving shuttles
10 Dutch cheese
11 Apply, as pressure
12 Zhou ___, prime minister of China 1949–76
13 Good grade: 2 wds.
14 Consisting of semiconductors: hyph.
16 Two-port electrical network element
17 ___ Magnon
18 "C'mon!": 2 wds.
22 Blunder
25 Hold up
26 1969 hit by the Who: 2 wds.
28 Mornings, initially
29 Greatest of ___: 2 wds.
32 Goliath was one
35 St. ___ Girl, Beck's Brewery offering
36 Synthetic fabric
37 Sneak ___: 2 wds.
38 Airheaded
39 Framework
40 Grand story

Down

1 Person's initials woven in a design
2 Method of starting play in field hockey: hyph.
3 Firefighter Red
4 "You ___ mouthful!": 2 wds.
5 Like a duck's feet
6 From one side only, in law: 2 wds.
7 Experienced
8 "___ Colors" (Cyndi Lauper hit)
9 John and Paul: abbr.
10 Some appliances, initially
15 Cardinal's insignia, initially
17 F/X animation
19 Collide with: 2 wds.
20 Spirit, pluck
21 Sounds of woe
23 More weak and delicate
24 Thin and slippery: hyph.
27 Manning or Whitney
30 Hebrew letter: var.
31 "Let ___!" ("Go ahead!"): 2 wds.
32 ___ John's (pizza chain)
33 Colored
34 "Tarzan" star Ron
35 ___-man (video game)

60

Across

1 Animal track
6 Onetime Golden Arches' offering
11 Cheyenne shelter
12 Gold braid
13 Most important boy- or girlfriend, slangily: 2 wds.
15 Match ender, for short
16 Suffix with chant or mass
17 "___ the winter of our discontent" (Richard III opening line)
19 "China Beach" setting, in short
22 Food eaten on a spring holiday: 2 wds.
24 Internet writing system with unconventional spelling
26 Eight: prefix
27 "Charade" actor: 2 wds.
31 Internet protocol inits.
32 Knitted scarf
33 Prefix with drama
34 Cove
37 Shrill: hyph.
41 Malayan boats
42 Final Commandment
43 Militant movement
44 ___ ghost (hallucinates): 2 wds.

Down

1 Bank acct. report
2 Pinnacle
3 First novel in Cather's "Great Plains" trilogy: 2 wds.
4 Vintner's prefix
5 Mends, as a bad stitching job
6 Puddinglike dessert
7 Algonquian Indian
8 "Still ___" (1999 rap song)
9 ___ Lemon, Tina Fey's "30 Rock" character
10 Lao-___
14 Give up
18 Like some high-fiber cereal
19 Juicy fruit
20 Contract negotiator: abbr.
21 Tropical fruit, briefly
23 Rice-a-___, the San Francisco treat
24 ___ Soundsystem, dance-punk band
25 Suffix with Jacob
28 Rock with colored bands
29 Be a monarch
30 Cancels
33 Assigner of Gs and Rs, initially
35 QB's misfires
36 Turkish leader
37 N.T. book
38 First name in Notre Dame football
39 Data storage site, initially
40 Gnarls Barkley member ___-Lo

61

Across

1 Leaves of a book
6 Indolent
10 N.F.L. Hall-of-Famer Hirsch
11 Dusk, old-style
12 Fertile soil
13 Rinse, as with a solvent
14 Suffix with cap or coy
15 Revival producer?: inits.
17 "It's cold!"
18 Pop's boy
19 Sch. in Tulsa, Oklahoma
20 52, in old Rome
21 "___ Came Back Again" (Johnny Cash song): 2 wds.
23 Temper, as metal
25 Five Nations members
27 Mountain lion
29 Narrow-waisted stinger
32 Online feed, initially
33 Fix, as a fight
35 Conflict
36 Flying expert
37 ___-Bilt (power tool brand)
38 Letters on some invitations
39 Great: prefix
41 Sewing cases
43 Civil War general defeated by Grant at Chattanooga
44 First five of 26
45 Skeleton part, in Padua
46 Powerful sharks

Down

1 First female House Speaker
2 Many: 3 wds.
3 Carbon dioxide, e.g.: 2 wds.
4 Selene's sister
5 Major food service company
6 "___ say!"
7 Twenty dollar bill, slangily: 2 wds.
8 Supreme worship allowed to God alone
9 Chef Lagasse who says "Pork fat rules!"
11 Coming or going, e.g.
16 Large open area of grassland
22 Chang's Siamese twin
24 "I don't think so"
26 Small elongated insect
27 Rhyming word game
28 Hollywood awards
30 Get married: 3 wds.
31 Non-poetic writing forms
34 Shine
40 First president of South Vietnam, ___ Dinh Diem
42 Not yet decided, initially

62

Across

1 Earth
5 They usually weren't hits: hyph.
11 Donald Duck, to his nephews
12 Vexes
13 Cheat
14 Lively pieces of music
15 Model agency co-founder: 2 wds.
17 Change gear in a vehicle
18 Fort Bliss city: 2 wds.
21 Smooth
25 Chou En-___
26 "All-American Girl" Margaret
27 "Every ___ Tiger" (Tom Clancy title): 2 wds.
29 Stamp, as a document
32 Connie's portrayer, in "The Godfather"
34 Early 20th-century depiction of the ideal woman: 2 wds.
39 "Lux aeterna" composer György
40 "Men of a Certain Age" star Richard
41 Spiritual knowledge
42 "Heavens to Betsy!"
43 Jean-Paul who wrote "Being and Nothingness"
44 Sleep roughly, in British slang

Down

1 Certain
2 "The ___ Love" (R.E.M. song): 2 wds.
3 Suffix with canon or comic
4 San Diego suburb: 2 wds.
5 Turkish bath-house
6 Take a whiff of
7 Bars of gold or silver
8 Gloomy
9 "Brown ___ Girl" (Van Morrison hit)
10 Draft org.
16 Hesitant syllables
18 American ___, state tree of North Dakota
19 When doubled, a Teletubby
20 Wrestling win
22 Flying expert
23 FDR home loan org.
24 U.S. currency unit: abbr.
28 Most optimistically: 2 wds.
29 Kay Thompson character
30 "Children of the Albatross" author
31 Drooped
33 Up and about
34 "Sesame Street" veterinarian
35 "Young Frankenstein" assistant
36 Othello's betrayer
37 Genetic strands, initially
38 Former Fords
39 T-shirt sizes: abbr.

63

Across

1 The Golden Rule, for one
6 Get on a Greyhound, e.g.
11 Late "City Slickers" actor Kirby
12 Disinclined
13 Buzzards, condors, etc.: 3 wds.
15 Arias, usually
16 Compete
17 Goose genus
19 Newt
22 Watergate, for one
25 Caesar's farewell
26 Irritable: hyph.
28 Disdainful grimace
29 Passages between rows of seats
30 Questionnaire question
31 "Don't change it"
32 Sneezy's colleague
33 Artistic inspiration
37 Having knowledge and spiritual insight
41 Repenting
42 Broke off
43 Anxious
44 Tiny thing, old-style

Down

1 Recedes, like the tide
2 Beethoven's "Archduke ____"
3 Cast
4 Point to
5 Businesses: abbr.
6 Fey
7 Brood
8 Measure
9 Indian tongue
10 Diffident
14 Be more skillful than
18 Hasten
19 Count, now
20 Beat it
21 Sen. Stevens and others
22 Levels a Luger
23 A lot of ice
24 Change
25 Clerical gown
27 Pandowdy, e.g.
31 Damp
32 Rackets
34 Computer "oops" command
35 Feel
36 Boating hazard
37 Horse-and-buggy ____
38 Roman Catholic sister
39 Bombed
40 Genteel affair

64

Across

1 ___-daisy: hyph.
5 Chip maker ___-Lay
10 "Go, ___!"
11 Pays
13 Time ___ half: 2 wds.
14 Lack of interest
15 Code in which many Web pages are written, initially
16 Whimsical idea
17 Cries from sties
19 "Help!": 2 wds.
21 Suffix with professor
24 Soft & ___ deodorant
25 George Strait's "All My ___ Live in Texas"
27 Photog.'s item
28 Marie, e.g.: abbr.
29 Steam engine noises
31 "Fingers crossed": 2 wds.
32 Ivanhoe's love
36 Some dishes on rooftops, initially
39 2,000 pounds: 2 wds.
40 Conductor Klemperer
41 Attractively full-figured, casually
42 Light and insubstantial
43 Timeworn
44 Suggestions on food labels, initially

Down

1 2002 Winter Olympics locale
2 Bottled (up)
3 It could make you weep: 2 wds.
4 Charlotte ___, capital of the Virgin Islands
5 Heart-to-heart: 2 wds.
6 Bank takebacks, briefly
7 "___ a loss to know what to do": 2 wds.
8 Evergreen shrub
9 Roman emperor after Galba
12 Dictionary entry: abbr.
18 "Melody Maker" alternative, initially
19 Certain 1960s protesters, initially
20 Dance, e.g.
21 Tainted, especially with disease
22 W.W. I army, initially
23 T-shirt sizes: abbr.
26 "___ 'nuff!"
30 Hullabaloo
31 One way to saute: 2 wds.
32 "Frasier" character
33 "Business Goes ___ Usual" (Roberta Flack song): 2 wds.
34 Fabric
35 "Roll With Me, Henry" singer James
37 Blade brand
38 Some beans

65

Across

1 Garment parts
8 "No use arguing with me": 2 wds.
9 Wall St. action
12 Fraudulent appropriation of funds
14 Do it wrong
15 Blissful
16 Comes (to)
19 Pollster's detection
20 Put into effect, as a law
22 Types of newsgroups, initially
23 Grasshopper's cousin
25 Haunting sound
27 Heaps
29 Train tracks
31 "___ (Understands)". Tammy Wynette song: 2 wds.
33 Distresses
35 By way of
36 Awkward situation
39 Prescription instruction, initially
40 Artist's paint-mixing board
41 Absorb the attention of

Down

1 Teams
2 Reinforcing rib used in Gothic vaulting
3 Given the right to vote
4 Tikkanen of the N.H.L.
5 Cruella de ___, 101 Dalmatians antagonist
6 Ending for effer or fluor
7 City in Germany
9 President's selective rejection: hyph., 2 wds.
10 Sound of a bounce
11 How some songs are sold: 2 wds.
13 In an curt manner
17 Released conditionally
18 "Nova" subj.
21 ___/IP
24 Actress Basinger
25 Blow one's top
26 Resort island off the coast of Italy
28 People of exceptional holiness
30 Michael of R.E.M.
32 Archibald and Thurmond of the NBA Hall of Fame
34 Diagnostic test
37 N. Afr. country
38 Mal de ___ (seasickness)

66

Across

1 Bacon, chicken and egg salad
5 Clock sound
9 "House" star Hugh
12 Like some textbook publishers: hyph.
13 Huge house and its grounds
14 Professional people: abbr.
15 Put to bed, as a child: 2 wds.
17 "Self-Reliance" author's monogram
19 F.D.R.'s successor
20 Rapper pal
23 Arrangement of a set of numbers in math
25 Highland dagger, ___ dhu
27 Coffee for insomniacs, perhaps
28 Acid present in apples
29 Become accustomed (to)
30 Concede
31 CenturyLink, for example: inits.
32 Fast no more
34 Clod
35 Threaded
37 Big name in photography, once
40 Game bird with feathered legs
43 Latvian, e.g.
44 "In ___ and out the other": 2 wds.
45 Social rebuff
46 "Dianetics" author Hubbard: 2 wds.

Down

1 A.L. Central city
2 Alliance created in 1948, initially
3 Common grassland plant
4 German beer
5 High schooler
6 Canadian TV channel, initially
7 Bill amt.
8 "___ For Killer" (Sue Grafton novel): 2 wds.
10 Tinea pedis may cause this: 2 wds.
11 Fun house sounds
16 1980 Jill Clayburgh movie: 3 wds.
17 Pie cuts, essentially
18 Small songbirds
20 Lay siege to
21 Berates
22 How some music is sold: 2 wds.
24 Rhine feeder
26 Chiang ___-shek
33 Mythical ship
35 Letters identifying a combination of voices (music)
36 "Mad Dogs and Englishmen" writer Coward
37 Crunch time targets, in short
38 Ramat ___ (Israeli city)
39 Swine ___
41 ___ Paulo
42 Directional suffix

67

Across

1 Fixes firmly
7 Azimuth
10 Grand ____
11 Lightly burn
12 Cuckoo
13 Highland tongue
14 Dines
15 Do some genetic engineering
17 Cottontail's tail
18 Garbage
19 African antelope with thick horns
20 Emerald, essentially
21 Coal carrier
23 Turn sour, say: 2 wds.
25 Fatigue
29 Soft pink
30 French rake?
31 Rub elbows
33 Scary beasts created by J.R.R. Tolkien
34 All fired up
35 Defensive barricade of felled trees
37 Adjusts, as a clock
38 Pinpoint
39 Bride's new title, perhaps
40 "Resurrection" composer Gustav

Down

1 Most cold
2 Monte Carlo's locale
3 Destroy, as a crime ring: 2 wds.
4 Fastening devices: 2 wds.
5 Cubby hole?
6 Palindromic candy company
7 Vaporize
8 Imp
9 Angler's basket
11 Contrition, remorse: hyph.
16 Keats, for one
20 Flower starter
22 Angelic circlet
23 Check the details: 2 wds.
24 Goes round the Earth, e.g.
26 Of the main artery
27 See-through sheet
28 Reduced
29 The Grand Canyon, e.g.
32 Bee ____
36 Big snake that squeezes its prey

68

Across

1 Jimmy Stewart syllables
4 ___ amis
7 Become inedible
8 First prime
9 Hole-making tool
12 Inquest official
14 Golfer Michelle
15 Saucepan's partner, sometimes: 2 wds.
16 "Wizards of Waverly Place" actress Gomez
18 Train stop
20 Well, in France
21 S.A.S.E., e.g.
22 Buffalo's AAA baseball team
25 Painful sore or ulcer
27 Prim partner
28 ___ favor (please, in Spanish)
31 Turner and others
32 Paris bisector
34 Discordant
37 Non- or un-: abbr.
38 Vietnamese beef broth soup
39 Marked by great fruitfulness
41 Many generations
42 Battery size letters
43 Negative link
44 "Top Hat" studio, initially
45 Fast sports cars, for short

Down

1 Place to play video games
2 Fleeced
3 Newspaper feature: 2 wds.
4 Matterhorn, e.g.
5 Rams' mates
6 Like some losers
9 Arousing a feeling of wonder: hyph.
10 Alcoholic drinks
11 Slender
13 ___ the Hero, wizard in "Harry Potter and the Half-Blood Prince"
17 Acquisition transactions, briefly
19 Cough syrup meas.
23 Curler's setting
24 Relig. deliveries
26 Deck crew's boss, briefly
27 Beginning of logic
29 Trading unit: 2 wds.
30 Directs (to)
31 Place to pick up a kitten
33 Skillful, competent
35 Miles away
36 Tap trouble
40 1990s Indian P.M.

69

Across

1 Cabbie's line: 2 wds.
6 Actress Pinkett Smith
10 Borrowed: 2 wds.
12 North Carolina university
13 Bounce back again: hyph.
14 Suffix with million or billion
15 Respectful Turkish title
16 Keyed up
18 Actresses Lucci and Sarandon
21 Not neat: 3 wds.
23 They go below signatures, for short
26 Vessel detector
27 Org. for Budge and Tilden: 2 wds.
29 Not hot anymore
30 Pioneering aviator Amelia
32 Derisive
33 Psychology pioneer Alfred
35 Economic standard used for comparison, initially
38 Popeye's "boy-kid" ___'Pea
39 Not alfresco
42 Brazilian soccer great
43 "I have found it" (Archimedes)
44 Heroic deed
45 Special Forces cap

Down

1 Circle dance
2 A thou, slangily: 2 wds.
3 Enjoyable
4 Games grp.
5 "Not gonna happen"
6 Hard-wearing pants
7 Actresses Landry, Lohan and Larter
8 French illustrator of Cervante's "Don Quixote"
9 Chemical suffix
11 ___ much (less)
17 Make certain
19 Thurman of "Dangerous Liaisons"
20 Unflappable
21 Equal: prefix
22 "___ Turn" (road sign): 2 wds.
23 Regular theater attendee
24 Narrow waterway: abbr.
25 Used a bench
28 NYSE purchase: abbr.
31 Falcon's home
32 Icy rain
33 ___ bit (slightly): 2 wds.
34 Creme-creme center: 2 wds.
36 "Okey-___!"
37 Prefix with fall
38 Tanning lotion letters
40 Gist
41 Literary gloom

70

Across

1 "On the Trail" composer Grofé
6 Big ____ outdoors: 2 wds.
11 Declare legally void
12 "If I ____ betting man… ": 2 wds.
13 Capital of Tanzania: 3 wds.
15 Four: prefix
16 Jerry Lewis's telethon org.
17 Gentle pat
20 Ed.'s requests
22 "American ____" (TV show)
24 "A Farewell ____": 2 wds.
28 Christmas season vehicle: 2 wds.
30 Belafonte and Lewis
31 Peut-____ (maybe, in Marseilles)
32 Mil. decorations
34 Initials, perhaps
35 Churchill's "so few", initially
38 When doubled, a seafood entree
40 Hate coupled with disgust
45 Arms' ends
46 Bend a senator's ear, perhaps
47 Actors Damon and LeBlanc
48 Kind of change

Down

1 Pet Rocks or Virtual Pets, e.g.
2 Disney deer
3 Time off, initially
4 The Everly Brothers, e.g.
5 Someone ____ (not yours)
6 Not in the dark about: 2 wds.
7 Partner of poivre
8 "Sabre Dance" composer Khachaturian
9 Advantage, in sports
10 Priest of the East
14 Respected leader in national or international affairs
17 Falls slightly
18 Biblical mother of Jabal and Jubal
19 Cold, violently gusty Adriatic wind
21 After-Christmas event
23 Fat for cooks
25 ____-Rooter, sewer repair company
26 Cleopatra's love ____ Antony
27 Holy Fr. women
29 Send away
33 "____ We Dance?"
35 Chicago mayor ____ Emanuel
36 Quatrain rhyme scheme, sometimes
37 Source
39 "Me as well": 2 wds.
41 Summer hrs. in Wyoming
42 Nigerian tribesman
43 Delivery room doctors, for short
44 Nevada county

71

Across

1 Covered in a shiny coat of gold
5 RBI or ERA, e.g.
10 Cropped up
12 "Vive ___!": 2 wds.
13 Chair toted on poles
14 Kind of terrier
15 Jewish eve
17 Part of G.M.T.
18 Cries at fireworks
20 In order (to): 2 wds.
22 "Lovely" Beatles girl
24 Represents: 2 wds.
28 Deal
30 "Do I ___ Waltz?" (Rodgers-Sondheim musical): 2 wds.
31 Storm clouds
33 Destroy
34 Safety org.
36 Tiny amount
37 Units of sound intensity
40 Marquis de ___
42 Of a region
44 Agreed-upon requirements
47 Two-time U.S. Open winner Fraser
48 Yemen's capital
49 Good ___: 2 wds.
50 Derriere

Down

1 Heating alternative
2 High dudgeon
3 Navigational aid
4 Abdicator of 1917
5 Western metropolis, initially
6 Trucker in a union
7 Indy driver Luyendyk
8 ___ Bora (Afghan region)
9 ___ Fein
11 Chemical suffixes
16 Feathery wrap
18 Sculpting, painting, et al.
19 Trumpet legend Al
21 German cry
23 Teetotaler's order: 2 wds.
25 Dessert wine
26 Diva's delivery
27 Hourglass contents
29 Flight board letters
32 Passports and such
35 "Carmen Jones" song: "___ Love"
37 Actor Eric
38 "___ tú" it's you, in Spain
39 Like some meat
41 "___ me!"
43 "Ben-Hur" author Wallace
45 Lamb's cry
46 Patriotic org.

72

Across

1 Tolkien creature
4 Long-running variety show letters
7 Cow comment
8 Memphis to Nashville dir.
9 Network with an "eye" logo
12 Place to be put up
13 Let go: 2 wds.
15 Heads of France?
17 Crown
18 "Now I've ___ all": 2 wds.
20 D-Day carriers, initially
21 Parisian lass, for short
22 Birth state of seven presidents
23 Oct. preceder
25 Call off
27 Deighton who wrote "The IPCRESS File"
28 Keep ___ profile: 2 wds.
30 Baseball's Tony or Alejandro
32 Bygone era
33 Iron attractor
36 Barcelona's country
38 Bullriding competition
39 Balcony
41 Parisian pronoun
42 Suffix with direct or deposit
43 +: abbr.
44 Japanese computer giant, initially
45 F.B.I. employee: abbr.
46 Irish sweetheart

Down

1 Leaves out
2 Blakley of "Lightning Over Water"
3 Belonging to the present
4 Stalkless
5 Opposite SSW
6 Baltic resident
9 Coming down with a bang: 2 wds.
10 Wodehouse's Wooster
11 Add spice to
14 Flaky pastry
16 The big picture?: abbr.
19 Two hrs. to midnight: 2 wds.
23 Tells: 2 wds.
24 One who runs off to wed
26 Most loved
29 Low dam
31 First president of South Vietnam, ___ Dinh Diem
34 Conger catcher
35 Puccini classic
37 California county or its seat
40 Wheel tooth

73

Across

1. ____ problem with (doesn't like): 2 wds.
5. Tower site
10. Cruise capitaine's stops
11. Tons: 2 wds.
12. Yr. before jr.
13. Buffaloes
14. Car safety device: 2 wds.
16. Bookbinding leather
17. Endings for can and caramb
21. Popular sandwich filling, initially: 3 wds.
23. Finger, in a way
24. Wolf chicken, e.g.
25. Egypt-Syria alliance, 1958–61, initially
27. Rock guitarist Steve
28. Sgts. and cpls.
30. Bog
32. Scand. country
33. Emphatic type: abbr.
34. One who can't remember
38. Montana and Bruce
41. Blood opening
42. Sign before Taurus
43. Slangy suffix for "buck"
44. One of Santa's reindeer
45. Depression

Down

1. Snake's warning
2. Hand cream ingredient
3. Threshing machine, e.g.
4. "Jobs" star Kutcher
5. Get-out-of-jail money
6. Hall-of-Fame Dodgers manager Walter
7. Half a gaffe
8. Suffix with Ecuador
9. Mormon letters
13. Jonson, Harrison and Franklin
15. "Mama's Gun" singer Erykah
18. Pendant necklace
19. One of a Latin trio
20. Tres y tres
21. Friend who founded a state
22. Celtic god of the boar
26. Memorization
29. "The ____ River" (Florida state song)
31. Giants' footballer Jennings
35. Bestselling PC game of the 1990s
36. "Supermodified" DJ Tobin
37. Cantankerous guy
38. Lancelot du ____ (knight of the Round Table)
39. Ending for pistol or haban
40. Game with matchsticks

74

Across

1 Donny and Marie, e.g.
5 Warning signals that wail
11 Dip ___ in (test): 2 wds.
12 List shortener: 2 wds.
13 Boxing prize
14 Learned person
15 Upgrade target: 2 wds.
17 Winnie-the-Pooh creator's monogram
18 Damage permanently
22 Fortresses
26 Prefix with bar
27 Did something wrong
28 "Be quiet!": 2 wds.
30 201, in Roman numerals
31 U2's "Where the ___ Have No Name"
33 Abbr. in many job listings
35 Laugh sound
36 Alternative to a bikini: hyph.
41 Firetruck feature
44 Easy as falling off ___: 2 wds.
45 Melodious
46 Filmmaker Riefenstahl
47 Places to sleep
48 Droops

Down

1 "Elephant Boy" boy
2 Ending for term or favor
3 Tree trunk
4 Predetermined cost: 2 wds.
5 Halvah ingredient
6 "Take ___ a sign": 2 wds.
7 Four-star reviews
8 "She" in Portuguese
9 "Delta of Venus" writer
10 Enjoyed the couch
16 Gets bare on top
19 Short-run film shower
20 ___ were (so to speak): 2 wds.
21 Deteriorates
22 Anatomical cavities
23 Parentheses, e.g.
24 Hindu titles
25 Dump into a Dumpster
29 Overhead photos
32 "Where ___ a will…"
34 Bustles: hyph.
37 Home, informally
38 Zeno of ___
39 D.C. group
40 Support: var.
41 Gibbon of Thailand and Malaysia
42 River of Venezuela
43 The Divine, to da Vinci

75

Across

1 "The Bold and the Beautiful" actress Sofer

5 More than plump

10 Altitudes: abbr.

12 Emcees

13 "A Room With ___": 2 wds.

14 Choral work

15 O-___-O (dishwand brand)

16 Rope in

18 Polynesian-themed restaurant chain, ___ Vic's

20 Sacramento newspaper

21 Put another hole in the barrel

23 "Pink Panther" films actor

24 Dear deer of film

26 Out of order

28 Hosp. units

29 Someone ___ (not yours)

31 Boom source, initially

32 Furthermore: 2 wds.

35 Barbecue spot

38 Classic British sports car

39 "Peace ___ time": 2 wds.

40 "Carmen," for one

42 Singer Ronstadt

43 Forty-___ (prospector)

44 Register: 2 wds.

45 Road-map abbrs.

Down

1 Flinch, perhaps

2 Young eel

3 Apollo 11 commander of 1969: 2 wds.

4 Blvd. cousin

5 Units of electrical resistance

6 Godsend

7 Formation, creation

8 Sound systems

9 Prizes highly

11 Term of endearment

17 Colt's fans, initially?

19 Entrant into society, briefly

22 Stick to (with glue): 2 wds.

24 "Quit fidgeting!": 2 wds.

25 "Coming to America" star Hall

27 Encountered

30 Word in many Quebec town names

33 Concur

34 Alpine lifts: hyph.

36 Fashion designer Gernreich

37 Island off Donegal

41 Area of a circle = ___-squared: 2 wds.

76

Across

1 To the left, at sea
6 Hit with an open hand
10 "Pipe down!"
11 Woods on the golf course
13 Get involved
15 Doctrine: suffix
16 Dividend earner: abbr.
17 You, abroad
18 More prepared
20 John, Paul and George, but not Ringo: abbr.
21 One, in Weimar
22 Jazz pianist Blake
24 ____ diem (seize the day)
26 "____ Like Her" (movie starring Lexi Ainsworth): 2 wds.
28 Cheese with a red coat
32 Bee: prefix
33 Harpsichord
35 Work ____ lather: 2 wds.
36 Fu-____ (legendary Chinese sage)
37 Fire up (the motor), shortly
38 Cultural rebirth from the 14th to 17th centuries
41 "Beyond Scared Straight" network: 3 wds.
42 One of the Muses
43 Narrow inlets
44 Synthetic fabric

Down

1 Wish, with "to"
2 First stage of an operation: 2 wds.
3 "____ Flint" (1966 James Coburn film): 2 wds.
4 Queue after Q
5 "Jesus loves me, ____ know": 2 wds.
6 Rider's foothold
7 Insolence
8 Andre of tennis
9 Diminutive
12 Arikaras
14 Dreary, without comfort
19 Metric prefix
23 BBC nickname, with "the"
25 Bunker and Goodwin
26 Materialize
27 Designer Versace
29 Charles ____, "A Tale of Two Cities" character
30 Sister of Tisiphone and Megaera
31 Progress: 2 wds.
32 Mystique, e.g.
34 Cheapskate
39 Nabokov novel
40 Former football coach Parseghian

77

Across

1 Egyptian snakes
5 When mastodons became extinct: 2 wds.
11 Surveyor's map
12 "Kitty Foyle" author Christopher
13 Madras dress
14 Red-blue color
15 Preacher of the gospel
17 Taken dishonestly
18 Corn to be ground
20 Protected bird
24 Wrestling milieu
25 Notable period
26 This and that
29 Half a sawbuck
31 Cover
33 Over-sentimental
37 Madison's successor
38 Barbados export
39 Cafeteria-goers
40 12th month of the Jewish civil year
41 Puts pen to paper
42 Camera piece

Down

1 Church alcove
2 Croat or Serb
3 Leech
4 Supplies an inadequate amount
5 Motivate
6 Washington's Grand Dam
7 Making a mistake
8 European mountain range
9 Money, slangily
10 Word with ball or socket
16 Inherited
18 Clock std.
19 Cheerleader's cheer
21 Military wake-up call
22 Up to, in sonnets
23 Road cover
27 Something only a few people know
28 Ovation elicitation
29 J.F.K. watchdog
30 Abba Eban's land
32 Board game
33 Fly high
34 Hostile to
35 Subject of a sentence, typically
36 Elusive ones
37 Kitten's plaint

78

Across

1 Tree that bears edible yellow fruits
7 Son of Noah
11 Disgrace, old-style
12 Rhine tributary
13 Cocktail fruits
14 Abbr. on folk music
15 Loose-fitting garment: 2 wds.
17 Quilters' do
19 Antitoxins
20 TV show interruptions
21 Feed
25 Conk out
26 Biological marker letters
27 "____ man walks into a bar…": 2 wds.
28 Arkansas and Arizona
30 Wedding vow: 2 wds.
31 Get better
33 Overseas carrier, initially
34 Assume a distinct form: 2 wds.
38 Shinzo ____, prime minister of Japan
39 Foreign heads of state: var.
42 "Penny ____" (Beatles song)
43 Broadcast receivers
44 Firm parts: abbr.
45 "I've got enough on my plate ____": 3 wds.

Down

1 "The Languages of ____" (Jack Vance novel)
2 Handy form of communication letters?
3 Inlet off the coast of Russia: 2 wds.
4 Cobble, for example
5 Church words

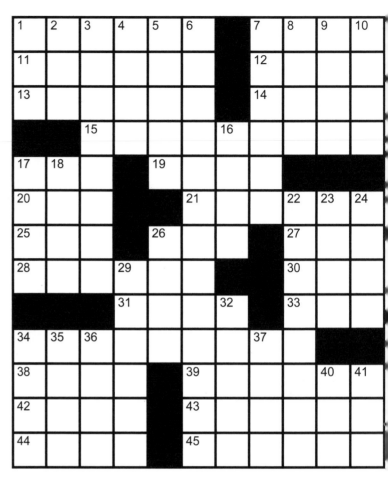

6 Region of northwestern Africa, capital Laayoune: 2 wds.
7 Petty bureaucrat
8 Fast loser
9 Perfect games improve them, initially
10 Drugs, briefly
16 Actress de Matteo of "The Sopranos"
17 Stench
18 Shorten a sentence, maybe
22 From my point of view: 4 wds.
23 Clubhouse drink
24 New Mexico art community
26 Barely passing grades
29 Luther posted 95
32 Mongolian monks
34 100 sene in Samoa
35 Like ____ out of hell: 2 wds.
36 County in the south of England
37 Foot: prefix
40 Charles le Gros, for one
41 Onetime lottery org.

79

Across

1 "___ Theme" (tune from "Doctor Zhivago")
6 Mentally acute
11 Coeur d'___, ID
12 Certain fisherman
13 Arrange and control for effect: hyph.
15 Tic-___ (metronome sound)
16 ___ Kan
17 Bad: Fr.
18 Loads
20 Say again, as a story
22 Soon, to a bard
23 Cold war grp.
24 City in a "Can-Can" song
26 "It's a pity": 2 wds.
30 Genre of popular music, initially
32 Doctor's prefix with -ologist
33 "Please stay!": 2 wds.
36 Be, at the Forum
37 Lennon in-law
38 President before JAG
40 Boarding place: abbr.
41 Extremely angry: 4 wds.
44 "___ not amused!": 2 wds.
45 "That's ___"
46 Second tries, casually
47 Marked with bands

Down

1 Race climax: 2 wds.
2 City in the Allegheny Mountains
3 Nuclear structure
4 Film director ___ Lee
5 Hunt for
6 Ability to walk on deck: 2 wds.
7 Egg warmer
8 "That's ___ excuse!": 2 wds.
9 Fit for a queen
10 Shampoo brand
14 Cleopatra's love ___ Antony
19 Hägar's pooch
21 Beef cut: hyph.
25 Occupy completely
27 Meeting
28 Hardly luxurious
29 Greatly feared
31 All-Star reliever Nen
33 Serve: 2 wds.
34 Cat ___ tails: 2 wds.
35 Famous
39 Make well
42 Familia member
43 "I don't wanna hear it!", initially

80

Across

1 Not up
5 Center of spiritual power, in yoga
11 First name in raga performance
12 Astronaut Collins
13 High cards
14 Atomic trials of the past, for short: 2 wds.
15 Opposing votes
16 Beer barrel poker
17 Aloha State state bird
19 Place for a lecture
23 Back-talker
25 Astringent fruit
26 Animated film unit
27 Mil. decoration
29 Author LeShan
30 Mars, to the Greeks
32 Hot topics of the day
34 Hardly the life of the party
35 North Dakota, to Pierre
36 Kind of agent: abbr.
38 Band events
41 Remove all metallic traces from
44 Wilde's "The Ballad of Reading ____"
45 "Tristram Shandy" author
46 ____'acte (break between two parts of a play)
47 Less binding
48 Brit. decorations

Down

1 Island off Donegal
2 ____ Noir (hybrid red wine grape)
3 "In the Body of the World" author: 2 wds.
4 Puts down, slangily
5 Baseball defense player: 2 wds.
6 ____ run of bad luck: 2 wds.
7 Hebrew letters
8 "Star Trek: Voyager" character
9 Done working: abbr.
10 Reply to a ques.
18 Grant-giving grp.
20 Some Unalaska residents
21 Mother ____ (big metals find)
22 Grazing sites
23 Line breaker
24 ____ Flite (bicycle brand)
28 Chi. hrs.
31 Exodus commemorations
33 Settled
37 Deadly poison
39 Call on: 2 wds.
40 Some cameras, initially
41 High-speed hookup, for short
42 D.D.E.'s arena
43 DiCaprio, to fans

81

Across

1 1974 John Wayne title role
4 Four-poster, for example
7 "Way cool!": abbr.
10 Top vineyard
11 Ending for lemon or lime
12 "Bravo!"
13 Gets ready: 2 wds.
15 Collagen injection site
16 Be paid for work
17 Prefix with -lithic
19 Founded: abbr.
21 Uncle ____ (rice brand)
22 Date
23 Soak in a liquid
26 Flightless birds
28 Adorn with ribbons, garlands, etc.
30 Jennifer Lien's role in "Star Trek: Voyager"
33 Pro____: proportionally
34 ____ Na, rock and roll group: 2 wds.
36 Tehran native
38 Envelope abbr.
39 Grimm character
40 Cutting down, in a way: 3 wds.
43 Phone trio on 3
44 Topper with a pompom
45 Gun gp.
46 Michaels and Yankovic
47 Get-____ (starts)

Down

1 Fibber and Molly
2 Origami feature
3 Old weapon of defense
4 Undergrad degrees, initially
5 E-address ending
6 "Pirates of the Caribbean" star
7 Gliding about on wheels: 2 wds.
8 Creatures from outer space
9 Get rid of, as a dictator
14 Genetic initials
18 What you might be as busy as: 2 wds.
20 ____-Honey (candy bar): hyph.
24 "O Sole ____"
25 Great heights, for short
27 ____ end (over): 2 wds.
28 Cooked in hot fat
29 Country rocker Steve
31 Prefix relating to the intestine
32 ____ Little Helper, Bart Simpson's dog
35 Owned
37 Infinitesimal amount
41 Ending with mater or pater
42 Some rush-hour periods: inits.

82

Across

1 Braved the odds
6 CBC news rival
9 City north of San Francisco, San ____
11 ____ little prayer: 2 wds.
12 Skirmish
13 Iowa State locale
14 Metal-lined wooden box used for transporting goods: 2 wds.
16 Good point
19 Solothurn's river
20 Literary category
21 Soprano's accolade
24 Italian monks
25 Latin 101 verb
26 Invite, as to one's appt.: 2 wds.
28 Bell town of literature
29 Brian of the early Roxy Music
30 Have a feeling
31 Unnecessary
34 "The Cherry Orchard" daughter
35 Fought over honor, maybe
39 Hunter's target
40 Divine syrup of Sikhs
41 "Really?" (letters in text-speak)
42 Short composition for a solo instrument

Down

1 "____ & the Women" (Richard Gere film): 2 wds.
2 Sports org. for nonprofessionals
3 Baseball number nines, briefly
4 It falls two days after Good Friday: 2 wds.
5 Erase data
6 He makes movies
7 Humorist Bill and comedian Louis
8 Cartoonist Thomas
10 Place for sheep to graze
11 Vast sandy region in North Africa: 2 wds.
15 Hack's vehicle
16 Kodak competitor
17 Church lectures, briefly
18 Throw of two ones with a pair of dice: 2 wds.
22 Moving vehicles
23 Dip ____ in (test): 2 wds.
27 Running expert, for short
28 Take on
31 California valley noted for its wines
32 Professor 'iggins, to Eliza
33 Author LeShan
36 Actress Lucy of "Elementary"
37 J.F.K. advisory
38 Jin-Soo Kwon in "Lost" actor, Daniel ____ Kim

83

Across

1 Dessert made of eggs and cream
7 ____ the crack of dawn: 2 wds.
11 Didn't go straight
12 Gangsters' guns
13 "____ later": 2 wds.
14 Others, to Ovid
15 Brownish purple
17 Ending for musket or mountain
18 Footwear ties
22 Mountain bike, for short
23 Line dance step: hyph.
26 Author of "The Shining": 2 wds.
29 Magazine feature
30 PBS supporter
31 Theater sceneries and props: 2 wds.
34 Suffix with ether or id
36 Death Row Records co-founder Knight
37 Backyard object
39 Slips
43 Went out, as a fire
44 Temblors
45 Drains, as energy
46 Famous chimney worker, briefly: 2 wds.

Down

1 Ed.'s pile
2 Bit of binary code
3 Ajman's locale, initially
4 Online call service
5 Asian capital
6 Estimate based on knowledge and experience: 2 wds.
7 Sch. in Athens or its bulldog mascot
8 Middle East region
9 "It's ____!" ("No-one wins!"): 2 wds.
10 Ivan the Terrible, for one
16 College course, casually
18 Backtalk
19 Letters before "://"
20 Stay too long in bed
21 "Yikes!"
24 Without ____ (daringly): 2 wds.
25 Major golf tourneys, initially
27 "Stupid ____ Tricks" (Letterman bit)
28 Tennis star Tommy
32 Cousin of a bittern
33 Small finch
34 Approximate takeoff times, for short
35 Mozart's "Il mio tesoro," e.g.
38 Begley and son
40 "____ Lay Me Down": 2 wds.
41 HBO alternative
42 Exhibit curiosity

84

Across

1 Of the sun
6 Admiral's command
11 Concert venue
12 Serve, in a way
13 Endangered Chinese mammals: 2 wds.
15 Cabinet Dept.
16 Tarzan creator's monogram
17 They protect QBs
18 Owe ___ of gratitude: 2 wds.
20 Hoopster
23 Enthusiastic cry
27 Peculiar: prefix
28 "Serpico" author
29 Orgs.
31 Breathers
32 Distiller's fruits
34 Capp and Capone
37 "High Sierra" actress Lupino
38 Meditation sounds
41 1890 battle site: 2 wds.
44 Musical with the song "Tomorrow"
45 Blackmore title name
46 Classroom furniture
47 Varieties

Down

1 Sizable story
2 At first: abbr.
3 "Laughable Lyrics" writer
4 Raggedy ___ (doll)
5 Not fit for kids, as a movie: 2 wds.
6 Having a spare tire, so to speak
7 Office computer system, initially
8 Edible corm of the taro
9 Airline to Tel Aviv: 2 wds.
10 "Dick Tracy" role
14 Historic leader?
18 Forever, seemingly
19 Makes less wild
20 Cloak-and-dagger org.
21 Super Bowl highlights, for many: abbr.
22 Soldiers, for short
24 Is down with
25 Feedbag bit
26 Org. in old spy stories
30 Moves smoothly along a surface
31 Checks the totals again
33 Thomas Hood's "Autumn," e.g.
34 Lots, as of bills: 2 wds.
35 Isolated
36 NBA team from Phoenix
38 "___ off?": 2 wds.
39 Noun suffix
40 Catches a glimpse of
42 Suffix with neat or beat
43 "Kitchy-___!" (baby tickler's comment)

85

Across

1 Florentine "Life of Christ" painter
7 Paper or plastic items
11 Rat (on)
12 Parmenides' home
13 Pippi Longstocking creator Lindgren
14 "Why not!"
15 Break a Commandment
16 Part of a plane: hyph.
17 Spoon-bending mentalist Geller
19 As yet unscheduled: inits.
21 Either or
22 Lose color
24 Fed chairman Greenspan
26 Enthusiastic and vocal supporter
30 Folky Williamson
31 River through Congo
32 Princess, initially
34 Furniture wood
36 Actress Dawn Chong
37 "The Cap and Bells" poet
39 Nile slitherer
41 ___ colada
42 Nearly
45 Abbr. on a business letter
46 Electronic device
47 Smell awful
48 In need of a nap

Down

1 Govt. property org.
2 Mental figures, familiarly
3 Remote possibility: 2 wds.
4 Garr of "Mr. Mom"
5 Dogpatch negative
6 Like an antique
7 Dracula Lugosi
8 Author of "An Essay on Man": 2 wds.
9 Welcome words to a hitchhiker
10 Impertinent
16 Brown rival
17 Martial arts promo. co.
18 Sound of support
20 Model material
23 Suffix with musket or market
25 Nonpro. sports org.
27 Ocho ___, Jamaican resort
28 Highest note in Guido's scale
29 Riddle-me-___
32 Keyed up
33 Queen of France
35 Superman's birth name: hyph.
38 Converse
40 Barrie buccaneer
42 Six-pack muscles, shortly
43 Back-to-school mo.
44 Have a go at

86

Across

1 First name at Gettysburg
4 "___ for the way you look at me" (line from a song): 2 wds.
7 Canadien, for short
10 Ending for web or video
11 Model Carol
12 Tuberous plant of the Andes
13 Shakespearean playhouse
15 Inability to stay focused, initially
16 Attack-trained military unit: 2 wds.
18 Great anger
19 Hi-___, stereo systems
20 Biological building blocks
22 "How did ___ thing like that happen?": 3 wds.
25 "___ Ha'i"
26 Invoice stamp
27 Loose talk?
29 Air Force installations
30 "That's cool!"
31 Waste watchers, initially
32 Wise ones: 2 wds.
37 Some batteries, initially
38 Equestrian footrest
39 Skid row woe letters
40 ___ Bo (Billy Blanks program)
41 Man-mouse connection: 2 wds.
42 Riddle-me-___ (rhyme)
43 No longer used, as a word: abbr.
44 Manuscript count: abbr.

Down

1 Fifth book of the New Testament
2 Thai money
3 TV celebrity chef from Louisiana: 2 wds.
4 Deli pancakes
5 The king, in Italian: 2 wds.
6 Tennis ace Graf
7 With a very raspy voice: 4 wds.
8 Flexible initials, electrically: hyph.
9 Enjoined
14 Passenger plane
17 Waterproof wrap: 2 wds.
20 "Touched by an Angel" network
21 Suffix with rep or rev
23 Windsor, for one
24 PennySaver pitches: abbr.
28 Annoys by persistent action: 2 wds.
29 Contradicts
32 Baghdad suburb: ___ City
33 Chess objective
34 Run up ___ (accumulate debt): 2 wds.
35 Many a northern Iraqi
36 Jacuzzis

87

Across

1 Upper limbs
5 Peeping Tom
10 Hard to comprehend
11 Afternoon: Sp.
12 Reclusive, unfriendly
14 Hazelton or Big Sandy, briefly: 2 wds.
15 The first "T" of TNT
16 Budget ___ System, Inc.: 2 wds.
20 Making a phone call, old-style
24 In days of yore
25 Up ___ (cornered): 2 wds.
26 Separated
28 Neighbor of Oman, initially
29 Extremely evil
31 Far from exciting
33 Moo ___ (Chinese dish)
34 Vouch for: 2 wds.
39 Uncontrollably noisy
41 Wisconsin college town
42 Basketball Hall-of-Famer Archibald
43 Eric Clapton classic
44 Safari sights

Down

1 Rehan, Lovelace and others
2 Let out
3 "Satan ___ Lady" (Bette Davis movie of 1936): 2 wds.
4 Saliva
5 Stay at home: 2 wds.
6 Walk back and forth
7 Minnie Driver's role in "GoldenEye"
8 Writer LeShan
9 Theologian's subj.
13 Similar things placed in order
17 "The Waiting" costar James
18 Culture starter
19 Drilling grp.
20 Unskillful painting
21 Stressed type: abbr.
22 Domain
23 Collect together in one place
27 Taking a break
30 Capital of Kazakhstan
32 Grasping, unpleasant woman
35 Device or implement
36 Coming ___ end (concluding): 2 wds.
37 1984 Peace Nobelist Desmond
38 Sugar suffixes
39 Dot-com's address
40 Airline to Karachi

88

Across

1 Dangerous slitherer
6 Ice cream drinks
11 Moves turbulently
12 Deals
13 Relief
15 Lux. neighbor
16 Crooked
17 Island of Alaska
19 "Dude!"
22 Rupp, Arco, et al.
25 Island known as "The Gathering Place"
26 Sportsperson not selected to play
28 Suffix with convert or digest
29 ___ Pieces (candy)
30 #19 in a series
31 Crude bed, to Brits
32 Is able to
33 "___ is the last straw!"
37 Hard work, say: 2 wds.
41 "Lorna ___"
42 Network, e.g.
43 Seemingly endless pit
44 Goes out with socially

Down

1 Egyptian, often
2 Big name in pineapples
3 Certain pickle
4 Grace, style
5 Bible translation published 1946–57, initially
6 Fire starter
7 Like Cheerios
8 601, to a Roman
9 ___ Z: 2 wds.
10 Tax form ID
14 "My mistake": 3 wds.
18 T, to Morse
19 Hammer sounds
20 Taekwondo great, Jhoon ___
21 "One of ___" (Willa Cather novel)
22 Anne Nichols hero
23 Civil War soldiers
24 Some blowups: abbr.
25 Aeschylus trilogy
27 1950s presidential race inits.
31 Coolidge's VP
32 Bamboozles
34 Male deer
35 "… a dagger which ___" (Macbeth): 2 wds.
36 Philly team
37 "When Your Child Drives You Crazy" author LeShan
38 Defensive shot, in tennis
39 Girl's counterpart
40 "Awesome!": abbr.

89

Across

1 Antiquing agent
5 Yitzhak of Israel
10 Prefix with -gon
11 Endeavor
12 Dadaist artists Jean and Hans
13 Small carnivore with a long slender body
14 Big swig
15 Ending for real or surreal
16 Thousand ____, Calif.
18 Brand of pet food
22 Black currant liqueur
24 Lovers' quarrel
25 Year in Nero's reign
26 Part of a play
28 Word with mouse or launch
29 Very much: 2 wds.
31 Persecute
33 Word on a wall, in the Bible
34 Adventurous Knievel
35 Chicago to Atlanta dir.
37 "The Unholy Wife" actress Diana
40 Common people (with "the")
43 Old fool
44 Clothing
45 "____ sow, so shall…": 2 wds.
46 Old Testament book
47 Beyond

Down

1 Captain ____ ("Moby Dick" character)
2 "American Gigolo" star
3 Detonation
4 They worship Jah, briefly
5 Short ways to go?
6 Estee Lauder fragrance line
7 Twice
8 "Now ____ heard it all!"
9 Classical pianist Anton
11 Gruyère, e.g.: 2 wds.
17 Asian automaker
19 Horse breed with a spotted coat
20 Peter who wrote "The Valachi Papers"
21 Yardsticks: abbr.
22 Burrowing marine mollusk
23 Drive train rod
27 Hebrew letter
30 "Twentysixmiles" actress Santiago
32 Railroad porter, familiarly
36 Hospital fluids
38 Baseballers Halladay, Campanella and White
39 Leave in, in proofreading
40 Start of a Chinese game
41 From ____ Z: 2 wds.
42 They're numbered in NYC: abbr.

90

Across

1 Happy ___ be: 2 wds.
6 Letters of introduction?
10 Flipped (through)
12 "I ___ Dark Stranger" (1946 movie): 2 wds.
13 More sharp
14 Contemptible sort, slangily
15 Most infrequent
17 Biol., e.g.
19 God, in Italy
20 Patty Hearst's captors, initially
23 TV teaser: abbr.
25 Pre-final software programs
27 Fast food restaurant chain: 3 wds.
28 Impact sound
29 Seven, in Spain
30 Private pupil
31 British sports cars, initially
32 Wall St. deal
34 Announcer Hall
35 Causes consternation
37 Hitch
40 Cooperate on a matter of mutual concern
43 Suffix with concession
44 Credit source
45 Cote sounds
46 Composer Camille Saint-___

Down

1 Key abbr.
2 Bering or Barents
3 Los ___, Granada, Spain
4 Skin conditioner brand
5 Lazy and irresponsible sort: hyph.
6 Busy exec.'s need
7 Big ___ (London attraction)
8 Corp. honcho
9 High-tech recording medium, initially
11 Three, to a German
16 Sad tales: 2 wds.
17 Tic
18 ___ T. Nelson, Hayden Fox of "Coach"
20 In the continental U.S.
21 Did up one's shoes
22 Set, as a price
24 Summer hrs. in Phoenix
26 Flightless bird from Down Under
33 Spherical object
35 Awfully long time
36 "Give that ___ cigar!": 2 wds.
37 Rest time: abbr.
38 Actress Vardalos of "My Big Fat Greek Wedding"
39 Legendary Notre Dame coach Parseghian
41 D.C. lawmaker
42 Where some nurses work, initially

91

Across

1 "N.Y.P.D. Blue" network
4 V-J Day pres.
7 Key state?: abbr.
10 Prefix with magnetic
11 One of Bo Peep's charges
12 Rio Treaty implementer, initially
13 Having a more piquant flavor
15 Hosp. areas
16 Surgical threads
17 Action on Wall St.
18 Sharp mountain ridge, to Pierre
19 "And your point being …?"
20 Point the finger at
22 Give a bad review to
23 Parasitic fly maggot
24 Scottish skiing surface
26 Neighbor of Scorpius
27 Void, in Versailles
28 Ford classics, familiarly: hyph.
30 Poet's "before"
31 Now, in Nicaragua
32 Tonic's partner
33 Musical
36 D.D.E. beat him twice
37 Personal belief or judgment
38 Due follower
39 The "L" of L.A.
40 Sault ___ Marie, Mich.
41 Alpine road shape
42 Biblical verb suffix
43 Get some grub

Down

1 PR people: abbr.
2 Male companion
3 Aids to vision: 2 wds.
4 Recipient of wealth
5 Increase one's offer, as in negotiations: 3 wds.
6 Short and often not sweet
7 State of happiness based on delusion: 2 wds.
8 Port side of a ship
9 Right after: 3 wds.
14 Wise adviser
20 Deny, renounce
21 Messengers
25 Get rid of
29 Flatten, in a way
31 "Make a mountain out of ___ hill": 2 wds.
34 Greek letter
35 Online tech. news resource

92

Across

1 1980s–90s show with Jimmy Smits: 2 wds.
6 "Ring Cycle" goddess
10 Come up
11 ___ Raton, Fla.
12 Historic ship: 2 wds.
14 Cpl.'s superior
15 "Citizen ___"
16 "Wheel of Fortune" purchase: 2 wds.
17 Mineral scale name
21 Painful sore or ulcer
25 Dried river bed
26 King and Norman
27 Lafcadio ___, U.S. journalist-author
29 ___ tai (rum cocktail)
30 Hillshire Brands company: 2 wds.
32 Dishwater
34 Cartridge holder
35 Get ___ deal: 2 wds.
37 Big snake
40 Act of pulling down
43 Like some D.A.s
44 "The Way I Feel" singer Remy
45 Card game start
46 In a snit

Down

1 Girl, in Scotland
2 As limp as ___: 2 wds.
3 Dryer deposit
4 Curaçao clock setting letters
5 Liability to failure under pressure or stress
6 Israeli statesman Abba
7 "Air Music" composer Ned
8 601 in Roman numerals
9 Good credit rating letters
13 Artist Nicolaes ___
16 Like a lot of clues in this puzzle: abbr.
18 Kind of agreement
19 Bring on at the company
20 Levelheaded
21 Donations
22 Loverboy
23 Came out with
24 Continually complaining or finding fault
28 Suffix with Jacob
31 "Come on, be ___!": 2 wds.
33 "Metamorphosis" protagonist Gregor
36 Unit of weight in some Muslim countries
37 Lack of equity
38 Suffixes with ball and bass
39 "Shadow Dancing" Gibb
40 Mommy's dearest?
41 Austin to Houston dir.
42 Meteorologist's comfort meas.

93

Across

1 The soft palate
6 Skip about playfully
11 Cordial flavoring
12 Israeli dances
13 Rocker Bob
14 "I Thought ___ You" (Miley Cyrus/ John Travolta song): 2 wds.
15 Devastation
17 Jack Bauer's org. in "24"
18 Trial figures, briefly
20 Arcade game, ___-Ball
22 "___ Carter" (Lil Wayne album)
23 Sworn statement
26 Antelope of the African savannah
28 Belgian painter James
29 One of the three superpowers in "Nineteen Eighty-Four"
31 ___-Cat (off-road vehicle)
32 Components of some PCs
33 Hammer part
34 Just right for the hole
36 Direct (to)
38 Bring down
40 "The Every Pain Reliever"
43 Strikes playfully with an open hand
44 Total body fitness system: 2 wds.
45 Four Holy Roman emperors
46 "Home Run" star Scott

Down

1 Anatomical vessel or duct
2 N.Y.C. to London dir.
3 Aviat Husky, e.g.: 2 wds.
4 "___ directed" (medicine alert): 2 wds.
5 "Wheel of Fortune" creator Griffin
6 Garbanzo
7 Internet company that merged with Time Warner in 2000
8 Legal paper presenter: 2 wds.
9 Right on the map
10 Between Q and V
16 Suffix with malt
18 Put ___ in (test the water): 2 wds.
19 Drive-___ (restaurant window)
21 Mighty long time
23 Psychological suffering
24 Top of the heap: hyph.
25 "Mission Earth" series author Hubbard: 2 wds.
27 Slot machine symbol
30 Serial suffix in Surrey
33 Bicycle part
34 Designer Rabanne
35 Border on
37 Destiny
39 BART stop
41 Nigerian native
42 Former Israeli airport name

94

Across

1 Mata ____ (spy)
5 Completely redone: 2 wds.
11 Chills, as champagne
12 Byzantine emperor 717–741: 2 wds.
13 Old school soda brand
14 Abhor
15 Chubby Checker hit of 1960
17 Latin trio center
18 "____ first…": 2 wds.
22 Nice touch
24 ____, zwei, drei
25 Old-school tough guys, in rap songs
26 ____ in the bud (catch a problem early)
27 "The Subject Was Roses" star Patricia
29 Roadside stops
32 Creator of Perry and Della
33 "Quo Vadis?" Oscar-winner Jannings
34 Star on a page
38 Hollow under the upper limb where it is joined to the shoulder
41 By an unknown author, in short
42 Sushi offering: 2 wds.
43 Editor's "strike-out"
44 Sister ____ ("We Are Family" singers)
45 Fantasy author Michael

Down

1 Clue
2 Banda ____ (Sumatran city)
3 Practice session in preparation for a public performance
4 "Am I the only one?": 3 wds.
5 "Frankenstein Unbound" author Brian
6 Vinter's dregs
7 ____ Moon, Baptist missionary to China (1873–1912)
8 Never, in Neuss
9 Dortmund dessert
10 Sense of humor
16 Isn't any more
19 Luxurious bedsheets, e.g.: 2 wds.
20 Blue dye
21 Dosage amts.
22 Christmas decoration
23 "Happy Days Are Here Again" composer Milton
28 Jumped
29 Grit
30 "Take Me Bak ____" (1972 Slade single)
31 Harangue
35 Victory: Ger.
36 Exchanged for money
37 Leg joint
38 Dummy
39 Catholicism or Judaism: abbr.
40 Fannie or Ginnie follower

95

Across

1 Matures
5 "Grace Under Fire" creator Chuck
10 Dash
11 Dog-___
12 Rat-___ (drumbeat): hyph.
13 "___ Hard" (John Lennon song): 2 wds.
14 Square hole made to receive a tenon
16 Perfect rating
17 Impetuous
21 To the rear
24 "Beat it, fly!"
25 ___ Vegas
26 "Send help!", initially
27 Nonsense syllables
29 Broad scarves
32 Yorkshire river
33 Ultimate degree
34 Went wild: 2 wds.
38 ___ pole
41 Alice's chronicler
42 Yoga posture
43 Triumphant cry: hyph.
44 Austrian spa town
45 Got 100% on

Down

1 "Gayane" composer Khachaturian
2 Spanish feline
3 Card game for two
4 Irish ___ (breed of dog)
5 Floral wreaths
6 Wild West movies
7 Monopoly quartet: abbr.
8 Legal thing
9 Old name for Tokyo
15 Place to stay
18 Mock phrase of comprehension: 2 wds.
19 It blackens a chimney
20 Big brother in "Bonanza"
21 Utah resort
22 Hindu wrap
23 Former ruler of Russia
28 Peaceful
29 Lily Tomlin's Edith ___
30 Several parallel layers of material
31 Sarkozy's predecessor
35 "I Am ___ of Constant Sorrow": 2 wds.
36 Like a shoppe
37 Natterjack
38 Q neighbor
39 She-bear: Sp.
40 Soupçon

96

Across

1 Doubly
4 Diamond or ruby
7 Chip off the old block
10 Generally: 3 wds.
12 "The Island of the Day Before" author
13 Given entirely to a specific person, activity or cause
14 Cries of surprise
15 Odd couple?
16 Native range horse
18 Minute amount
20 Key of Mozart's "Odense" Symphony: 2 wds.
22 Casual rejections
26 Engine part
27 "___ for apple": 2 wds.
29 Ending with exter or inter
30 Brim
32 Gesture of respectful greeting, for women
34 Edict
36 Opens up for the doctor, perhaps: 2 wds.
39 Horse's motion
42 "Hold On Tight" rockers, initially
43 New Brunwicks' river
45 Dormitory heads, for short
46 Certain female wild cat
47 Small island
48 Tarzan creator's monogram
49 U.S. 101, e.g.: abbr.

Down

1 1990s pop group Color Me ___
2 "Aha…": 2 wds.
3 Find a shortcut: 2 wds.
4 Beer drinker's stomach
5 Certain hot seat: 2 wds.
6 Cross, maybe
7 Former Chargers/ Patriots linebacker Junior
8 Big name in newspaper publishing
9 Bridge site
11 Fiddler's need
17 Hankering
19 ___ fault: 2 wds.
20 Make believe
21 Common female middle name
23 Aardvark
24 Lived
25 Foxy
28 Big ___, Calif.
31 OB/GYNs, e.g.
33 Adjust, as a brooch
35 Animation artist Eyvind
36 Antivenins
37 Asia's Trans ___ mountains
38 Kansas City Royals manager Ned
40 Section in the credits
41 Start of Massachusetts' motto
44 Burgle

97

Across

1 Tokyo's former name
4 Byrnes of "77 Sunset Strip"
7 Drift into dreamland
10 Skip of a stone on water
11 Notched like a saw
13 Michael J. Fox's role on "Family Ties": 2 wds.
15 "Rebel Without a Cause" costar Sal
16 "Revelations" choreographer Alvin
17 Some tourneys: hyph., abbr.
19 Padre's brother
21 Finishes, slangily: 2 wds.
25 Including unappealing features: 3 wds.
28 Brightest star in Aquila
29 Victory sign
30 City with canals
33 Theaters, slangily
36 Los ____ (city in western CA)
39 Bat-and-ball sport: hyph.
41 Show how it happened
42 Co. that produced "Lou Grant"
43 Summer setting letters
44 ____-cha chicken (Chinese menu dish)
45 Sister of Helios in Greek mythology

Down

1 Dutch cheese
2 Surrealist painter Salvador ____
3 International trade harbor: 2 wds.
4 Finland's second-largest city
5 Prefix meaning "ten": var.
6 "Get real!": 2 wds.
7 Abbr. in many org. names
8 Missouri River native
9 Say it never happened
12 Elevated
14 Generation ____: hyph.
18 Not give ____ (don't care): 2 wds.
19 Airline until 2001, initially
20 Potent or penitent ending
22 Be more efficient: 2 wds.
23 ____-de-France
24 Phillies and Braves grp.
26 Alehouse
27 Naps in Navarre
31 "Can ____ Witness" (Marvin Gaye song): 3 wds.
32 Low- or no-follower
33 Heavy string
34 "A Little Bitty Tear" singer Burl
35 Nair's former competitor
37 Catch ____ (start to get)
38 Sch. periods
40 Coolidge's successor, initially

98

Across

1 Whaler's adverb
5 ___ l'oeil
11 Vintner's prefix
12 Patch up
13 "___ a Teenage Werewolf": 2 wds.
14 1972 Jack Lemmon comedy
15 Springs
17 And others: abbr.
18 Builds a stock, in case of need: 2 wds.
20 S. ___, 40th state
21 ___ in "Oscar": 2 wds.
22 Boom box button, briefly
24 Qty.
25 Departure's opposite: abbr.
26 Catch red-handed
29 Scrape (out)
30 ___ manner of speaking: 2 wds.
31 Nile biter
34 High-school hand-ins
36 French beverage
37 Put a new label on, say
38 Devours with delight: 2 wds.
40 Metered vehicles
43 Cactus feature
44 Barbra's "A Star Is Born" costar
45 Business marriage
46 "Milk" director Gus Van ___

Down

1 Parisian pronoun
2 Chop
3 Someone skilled in interpreting data
4 Romantic flowers
5 Mead loose-leaf binder brand: 2 wds.
6 Races the engine, briefly
7 W.W. II org. 1941–7
8 Like a horse or lion
9 Ground-dwelling tropical bird
10 World Poker Tour champion Lindgren
16 Surrounding glows
18 Mauna ___ (Hawaiian volcano)
19 Weapon fired from a plane, initially
23 Colgate rival
26 Famous Falls
27 One, some or all
28 Undergrad degs.
31 Mr. T's group of the 1980s: hyph.
32 Part or portion
33 ___ Pan (peanut butter brand)
35 Axes
37 Hold sway over
39 Soak, old-style
41 Recycling container
42 Fast plane, for short

99

Across

1 Dominik "The Terminator" of hockey
6 Cousin of "ahem"
10 "___ Lucy": 2 wds.
11 Designer noted for an innovative series of chairs
12 Dancer Carol
13 Move stealthily
14 Ready for any eventuality: 3 wds.
16 Gallic goodbye
17 Fast jets, for short
20 Starter's words: 2 wds.
24 Run-___ (some sentences)
25 Resistance unit
26 Many college grads, for short
27 Gets on a ship
29 Blanchett of "The Aviator"
30 "Time is money," e.g.
32 Place for convalescents
37 Blue-ribbon position
38 Gaynor of "South Pacific"
39 Tee off
40 Name on jetliners, once
41 Judge
42 It may be perfect

Down

1 Snack cracker brand: hyph.
2 Rickman of "Galaxy Quest"
3 Prefix with gram or meter
4 At the very moment when: 2 wds.
5 Excited, with "up"
6 End up, conclude: 2 wds.
7 Hook's accomplice
8 Seven ___
9 "That wasn't nice!"
11 Put on a pedestal
15 Expresses sadness with: 2 wds.
17 Cry uncontrollably
18 ___-Caps (Nestle candy)
19 Org. that restricts liquids on flights
21 Maria Contreras-Sweet's organization, initially
22 Grab a bite
23 Taoism founder Lao-___
25 Peculiarity
28 Money demanded by a kidnaper
29 Red shade
31 Range
32 Kind of curve
33 Duncan appointed to the Obama cabinet
34 Make ___ adventure: 2 wds.
35 Commando weapons
36 Entangle
37 Beanie Babies, e.g.

100

Across

1 Mil. aides
5 Local dialects
11 One ___ (ball game)
12 Eritrea's capital
13 Heavy type of music: 2 wds.
15 Makers of counterfeit money
16 Somme time
17 Accord and Civic maker
18 Ed.'s requests
19 Junior high subj.
20 Prickly desert plant
23 ___ Sanger, Wikipedia co-founder
24 Drink with an umbrella: 2 wds.
26 The Divine, to da Vinci
29 Like some eagles?
30 Concealed
32 Tulsa sch. named for a televangelist
33 Manages: 2 wds.
35 Persuasion: hyph.
37 High-ranking
38 "So Big" and "Show Boat" author Ferber
39 Courses for horses
40 Those, to José

Down

1 "Aha!"
2 Educational institution
3 Rowing (a boat)
4 Bear
5 Bert who played the Cowardly Lion
6 Schools of thought
7 "Melody Maker" alternative, initially
8 Elaborate cake
9 Takes to the soapbox
10 Cut-price events
14 Marine otter: 2 wds.
18 It's often sloppy
21 Faint constellation next to Scorpius
22 "Ye gods!"
23 Jar part
24 Vandal, e.g.
25 College graduate
26 Sci-fi figures, briefly
27 "Beats me!": 2 wds.
28 Give off as vapor
29 Show off
31 Cosmetics maker Lauder
33 Cute creature in "Return of the Jedi"
34 Drinks of white wine and blackcurrant
36 Muscular twitch

101

Across

1 Elbowroom
6 Gets rid of, as extra weight
11 Toward the back
12 Military V.I.P., slangily
13 Trunks
14 2001 Nobel Peace Prize winner Kofi
15 Uneven, patchy quality
17 ___ Ste. Marie, Mich.
18 "Off ___?": 2 wds.
20 Divulges information: 2 wds.
25 Bundles of straw
27 Active people
28 Lisa, to Bart
30 Russian car make
31 Little laugh: hyph.
33 Clean slate
38 "Belling the Cat" author
39 Sister of Zsa Zsa and Eva
40 Big, in prefixes
41 Country album?
42 Many a "Roswell" character
43 Vichyssoise veggies

Down

1 Major sch. exams
2 Brace
3 Sprays
4 Clicker
5 Noted Verdi aria: 2 wds.
6 At an angle
7 Perfect, as a skill
8 A long, long time
9 Kaitlyn ___, voice of Riley in "Inside Out"
10 D.C. V.I.P.
16 Cook Co.'s home
18 Delivery room doctors, for short
19 Style of music, a fusion of Arabic and Western elements
21 Stand
22 Coastal flier: 2 wds.
23 California's Fort ___
24 Eavesdropping org.
26 Attacked: 2 wds.
29 Shepherd's field: abbr.
32 Turkish burden bearer
33 Blue-green
34 Fungal spore sacs
35 "It's such a ___ Being always Poor" (Langston Hughes)
36 Badlands Natl. Park locale: 2 wds.
37 "The law is ___…" (Dickens): 2 wds.
38 G.P. gp.

102

Across

1 Army unit of two or more divisions
6 Swiss river
10 Et ____
11 Street ____ (rep)
12 Egypt or Japan, e.g.: hyph.
14 Legal conclusion?
15 Org. for dentists
16 Coal carrier
17 Presidential periods
19 Units of distance
21 U.S. Army medal
22 Small change
23 Put up
25 Brute
27 Papeete's island: abbr.
30 Performs high-tech surgery
31 Indiana basketball player
33 Sounds of hesitance
34 Eastern concept
36 Dernier ____ (the latest thing)
37 Guy who lops branches: 2 wds.
40 One of the Sinatras
41 Collected
42 Glimpsed
43 Ways into a mine

Down

1 Discontinued
2 Freshwater carnivorous mammals
3 Outdoor goods retailer
4 Indonesian outriggers
5 Arabian capital: var.

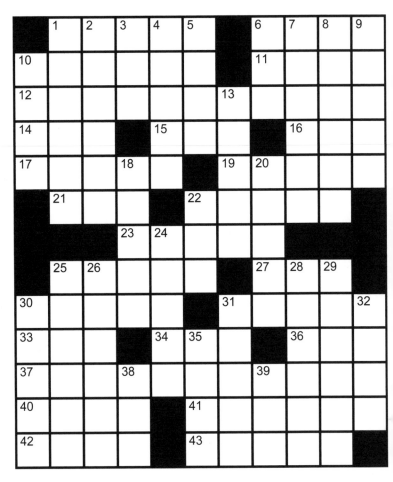

6 Play a role
7 Like farmland
8 Does up the laces again
9 Idyllic spots
10 Online technical news source
13 Tournament round
18 Major League Baseball player Brian
20 "____ Man" (John Ciardi poem): 3 wds.
22 Morse minimum
24 Helpers: abbr.
25 Creator of Peter Pan
26 Monk of yore
28 Receive willingly
29 Courageous men
30 Riga natives
31 Read (over)
32 Orange throwaway
35 Certain something
38 Suffix with Euclid
39 Moo goo ____ pan

103

Across

1. "There's ___ like home": 2 wds.
8. G.P.'s grp.
11. Rings of color
12. ___-Man (arcade game)
13. Back-to-school purchases
14. El stop: abbr.
15. Small, horned viper
16. Dietary, in ads
17. Alda or Arkin
20. Crops up
22. Gun sound
23. Allow
24. MS. enclosures
26. Greek porticoes
30. Charley ___, author of "The Winning Hitter"
32. Fibster
33. Ledger column
36. Classic street liners
37. Actress Arthur and others
38. "Curb Your Enthusiasm" channel
40. Gasteyer of "Mean Girls"
41. Stinkers
45. Corn holder
46. "Coming to America" star Hall
47. Art, to Tacitus
48. Requests: 2 wds.

Down

1. Scot's "not"
2. Bruin legend Bobby
3. Little green vegetable
4. Largest city in California: 2 wds.
5. Brewpub choices
6. Wristbone-related
7. Suffix with adopt or address
8. Orbital point
9. Dull photography finish
10. Rosacea and others
16. Small children: 2 wds.
17. Crunch targets, briefly
18. When doubled, a Teletubby
19. Ques. response
21. Notes after dos
25. Modeled (for)
27. Crude liquid
28. Way to shoot down a plane, initially
29. L.S.A.T. takers
31. Aisle escorts
33. Manila hemp fiber
34. Mexican mister
35. Swedish cars
39. Soak up the sun
41. Lamb's lament
42. Foot soldiers: abbr.
43. Kiddie-song ending letters
44. Campus women's org.

104

Across

1 Moribund, perhaps
4 Texas-based flyer, initially
7 ___-Man (arcade game)
10 Risk assessors' group, initially
11 Islamabad's country: abbr.
12 Elvis's record label, initially
13 Peak stat
14 Got down
15 One-time truckers' watchdog, initially
16 Property receiver
18 Butterfly catcher
19 Corroborate
20 Fort Collins sch.
21 Extra parts
22 1940s first lady
23 ___ cocktail, homemade missile
25 "Très ___!"
27 Dramatic or exciting conclusion
30 Airport abbr.
31 Metal marble
32 My follower
33 More technologically obsessed
34 Driver's ID: abbr.
35 "Wheel of Fortune" buy: 2 wds.
36 "Exodus" role
37 Drunk-skunk connection: 2 wds.
38 Inflamed
39 Helmsman's heading letters
40 Hangout
41 Hems and haws?
42 Prefix with mite or minus

Down

1 Naismith Memorial Basketball Hall-of-Famer John
2 Walk with a bounce
3 Nicaraguan, e.g.: hyph.
4 Breed of dog
5 Substance that gives more sudsing power: 2 wds.
6 Eddie's "Coming to America" role
7 Hal Foster's comics hero: 2 wds.
8 Admission
9 Prickly plant in Arizona
17 Actor Zac ___
22 Filleted
24 Vehicle's steering gear parts: 2 wds.
25 Minstrel's offering
26 Texas hold 'em pronouncement: 2 wds.
28 Cross-rib in vaulting
29 More scary
31 Animal catcher

105

Across

1 Cornerstone abbr.

5 Bond girl Ekland

10 Dress cut: hyph.

11 Like some cycles

12 Suggests

13 Chief Vedic god

14 High school subj.

15 Hoosegow

17 News org.

18 Part of some e-mail addresses

19 1988 NFL MVP Boomer

21 Fusses over oneself

23 Great heights, for short

24 He secures certain favors

26 Cassette contents

28 ____ Tomei, Kate in "Love Is Strange"

31 "Lou Grant" actor: 2 wds.

33 D.D.E. beat him twice

34 Leather shoe, for short

35 Some hosp. cases

36 Mil. titles

37 Secret, personal

39 Question asked twice in Matthew Chapter 26: 3 wds.

41 First word of a counting rhyme

42 Deceive, trick

43 ____ Philbin, Kelly Ripa's co-host

44 "The Mocker Mocked" painter Paul

Down

1 "Father Knows Best" actress Donahue

2 Text layout without much between lines: hyph.

3 Stick with a kick, shortly

4 Come down

5 Russian pancake

6 Score on the diamond

7 Develop manufacturing production on a wide scale

8 Large, silvery game fish

9 Teaches (a skill)

10 Scads: 2 wds.

16 Supposed to be the case

20 Part of A.C.L.U.: abbr.

22 Some shoe sizes

25 Affected by nausea in a vehicle

26 Sudden outburst of anger

27 Actress Renée of silent movies

29 Parlor piece

30 Guilty ____ (definitely not innocent): 2 wds.

32 "The Highwayman" poet Alfred

38 Seven, on a sundial

40 The Sun

106

Across

1 Palm fruit
5 Barcelona bar food
10 Manhattan Project goal: hyph.
12 "Diciembre" follower
13 Sealy rival
14 Slowpoke
15 Letter-shaped opening in some pistons: hyph.
17 Dundee denial
18 Nigerian tribesman
20 Madison, N.J., school, for short: 2 wds.
22 Simple soul
24 Airport in Washington: hyph.
27 "Somebody ___ Guy" (Jocelyn Brown single)
29 Prince album "___ the Times": 2 wds.
30 Get angry, say: 2 wds.
32 Old Chinese money
33 "I ___ Man Die" (Scarface single of 1994): 2 wds.
35 J.F.K. alternative
36 Yiddish word of disgust
38 Plant of the heath family
40 "Mefistofele" role
42 Filing material
45 Grant
46 Narrow and deep valley
47 Narrates, as a story
48 Part of S.S.S.: abbr.

Down

1 They prosecute wrongdoers, initially
2 Marge's father-in-law on "The Simpsons"
3 Semitransparent carapace of certain turtles
4 Initial response team, initially
5 End-of-semester students, often
6 Common girl's name
7 Top balcony in a theater, slangily: 2 wds.
8 Diva's solo
9 Only
11 Like old tires, maybe
16 Surgery sites, initially
18 Spanish model Sastre
19 Cotton unit
21 "Hold it!"
23 Comrade, old-style
25 Rare blood type: abbr., 2 wds.
26 Bubbly drink with caffeine
28 Oscillates
31 ___ lab letters
34 "Break ___!" (to an actor): 2 wds.
36 Exploit
37 "Heroes" heroine Bishop
39 Andy's radio partner
41 Lon ___, Khmer Republic president in the 1970s
43 QB protectors
44 Hitherto

107

Across

1 ___ Man, Tony Stark's alter ego
5 Greek letter that's also an airline
10 After "front" or "back," half of a golf course
11 Grain used for food
12 Freshman, probably
13 Equally hard to locate: 2 wds.
14 Awesome
16 Indulge in excessively, for short: 2 wds.
17 Weather map line
19 One in a bonnet?
21 Wailer
25 Pre-1975 power agcy.
26 Italian playwright Betti
27 Browser bookmark, initially
28 Put on clothes
30 Half-___ (coffee mix): abbr.
31 On the line: 2 wds.
33 Left, on a liner
36 "Juno and the Paycock" playwright Seán
39 Lubes anew
41 "Give ___ further thought!": 2 wds.
42 Access
43 52 cards
44 "New Girl" actress Deschanel
45 1968 folk album

Down

1 QB's misthrows
2 Modern waltz violinist André
3 Like some bathing suits: hyph.
4 Hawaii state birds
5 ___ Moines
6 Faults
7 Guide
8 South Seas starch
9 Architect William Van ___
11 Fragrant flower with pink blooms: 2 wds.
15 Full of vigor
18 Like certain battery terminals
19 Evil
20 Suffix with musket
22 Door-to-door salesman
23 Laundry room brand
24 ___ on the Shelf (Christmas figure)
29 Literary genre
32 "Somebody ___ Prayer" (Billy Ray Cyrus single): 2 wds.
33 Obama, slangily
34 Prefix with -phile
35 ___-tiller (cultivator)
37 Env. in an env., e.g.
38 Artist Ono
40 ESPN broadcaster Bob

108

Across

1 Sound of satisfaction
4 Lamb's mom
7 Salt lake in the Jordan valley: 2 wds.
9 Get the point of
12 Au courant
13 Triangle part: abbr.
14 Café additive
15 Afrikaners' village
16 Certain league: abbr.
18 Marshmallow, chocolate and cracker snacks
20 Bit of sunshine
21 Organism
22 Rate at which computer data is transferred, initially
23 30-second spots on TV
24 201 in old Rome
27 Shocks with a device
29 Coin flip call: abbr.
30 Vaughan, McLachlan and Bernhardt
32 "A Boy Named Sue" singer
33 Greek goddess Athena ___
34 1982 movie set in a computer
36 Ltd., in Paris
37 Attending: 2 wds.
40 Kit ___ bar
41 Current
42 Writer Rand
43 Internet protocol, initially

Down

1 Palindromic woman's name
2 New Testament book: abbr.
3 London road noted for private clinics: 2 wds.
4 "Freejack"'s Morales
5 Musical inspired by "Romeo and Juliet": 3 wds.
6 Chow down
8 ___ John
9 Cheated, in a way
10 Brontë governess
11 "The Mod Squad" costar, 1999
15 Get into
16 Wall Street figure, for short
17 It'll show you the way
19 "A rolling stone gathers no ___"
21 Brits' wingding
25 Record store purchases, shortly
26 Bull or fool follower
28 Bond rating initials
30 Bag for potatoes
31 Inter ___ (among others)
32 Hustles
35 Nothing: Fr.
37 Transcript fig.
38 Old cable inits.
39 Fifth qtrs.

109

Across

1 Part of a necklace
5 Devours
9 Odysseus's faithful dog in "The Odyssey"
11 Ford's predecessor
12 Large wading bird
13 Global health services organization
14 PepsiCo soft drink brand
15 Introduce
17 "The X-Files" extras, initially
18 "The Daughter of Time" writer Josephine
19 ___ Fail, Irish coronation stone
20 "Hail the Conquering Hero" actress Ella
22 Malt kiln
23 Penned up
25 West Point, for short
28 "Slavonic Dances" composer
32 Prefix with conservative or classical
33 Feed lines to
34 Ending for north or south
35 Like some pottery
37 Big foot meas.
38 Japanese beer brand
39 Violin stroke: hyph.
41 Dependable
42 Philadelphia suburb on the Main Line
43 Hydrocarbon suffixes
44 Three-handed card game

Down

1 Source of support
2 Typos
3 Eight-time Grand Slam champion
4 Quixote or Cornelius
5 Auspices: var.
6 Actress Bassett
7 Court sport
8 Try to hit: 2 wds.
10 Composition for seven musicians
11 ___-deucey (backgammon variant)
16 Remainder
21 Govt. code breakers
22 "Star Trek: Deep Space Nine" shapeshifter
24 Counterbalance: 2 wds.
25 Apprehension
26 Spring or summer
27 Prevailing mood
29 Adidas subsidiary
30 Colorful anatomical ring
31 "You can't fool me!": 2 wds.
33 Scolded
36 Not that
40 Loudspeakers, briefly

110

Across

1 "Cosmos" author Carl
6 Like
10 Make tight
12 Ascend
13 Nepal or Japan, e.g.: hyph.
15 Memory: prefix
16 Santa's little helpers
19 "Deadwood" figure
23 Blue
24 Bakery chain
26 Dentist: 2 wds.
29 Caldwell and Bernhardt
30 Nashville-based awards org.
31 Starchy foodstuff used in making puddings
32 "____ of pottage" (what Esau sold his birthright for): 2 wds.
34 Racers' goal, sometimes
36 Stargazers: hyph.
43 Gray and Candler
44 "Sesame ____" (kids' show)
45 Eleanor's successor
46 Button ____ (sewing machine fixture)

Down

1 Place to get off: abbr.
2 Bumper sticker letters
3 Kind of instinct
4 Once upon ____: 2 wds.
5 Bright fish
6 Music, paintings, etc.
7 Sedona maker
8 Follower's suffix
9 Born, in society pages
11 Weather report, initially
14 Drag through the mud
16 Those, in Mexico
17 "____ Theme" ("Doctor Zhivago" song)
18 Las Vegas hotel and spa
20 "The Hulk" director Lee
21 Ex-model Gabrielle
22 High school balls
24 Boil fluid
25 Literary collections
27 Fall back
28 Immunizations
32 Beat ____ to one's door: 2 wds.
33 An "M" in M-G-M
35 1950s election monogram
36 Popular dog, for short
37 Carbohydrate ending
38 Professor's helpers, shortly
39 "____ Constitution"
40 Moray, e.g.
41 Riddle-me-____ (rhyme)
42 Bering, e.g.: abbr.

111

Across

1 Stew ingredients
5 Feudal estate
9 Motocross participant
11 Tired of the world
12 Khomeini, for one
13 Northern Indians
14 Suffering: 2 wds.
16 Fast times
17 Postulate
20 "Slaves of New York" author Janowitz
24 "Perfect!" NASA-style: hyph.
25 Middle X of X-X-X
26 Proof word
28 Item found in a basement
31 Grammarian's concern
33 Not wearing a hat
38 "You've got mail" hearer
39 Bring up, as an issue
40 Succinct
41 As of
42 Has ___ with (is connected): 2 wds.
43 Marsh growth

Down

1 Toyota hybrids
2 Take home, as money
3 Mil. school
4 Dotty with age
5 Dense woodland
6 Fleur-de-lis
7 Some shoe sizes
8 They house engines, for short
10 Part of a stairway
11 Pigeon fancier on "Sesame Street"
15 Rubble maker, initially
17 Tooth-doctors' org.
18 Campus women's org.
19 Music style similar to reggae
21 Sporting figure: abbr.
22 Daisy ___
23 From side to side: abbr.
27 Deep dish
28 "Do ___ Diddy Diddy" (1964 hit)
29 Anxiety and trauma, for some
30 Bracing coastal atmosphere: 2 wds.
32 Lord's worker
33 "___ in the U.S.A." (Springsteen album)
34 "Others" in a Latin phrase
35 Have a sumptuous meal
36 Ending for evan or lumin
37 Owner's acquisition
38 Legal letters

112

Across

1 Job for a barrister
5 Mystic, supernatural
11 CDs and LPs
12 Gadabout
13 The "E" of Q.E.D.
14 Neighbor of Lebanon and Egypt
15 Mach 1, e.g.: 2 wds.
17 My, in Marseilles
18 Front tooth
22 Effort
24 Extreme violence
25 "Thereby hangs ___": 2 wds.
27 Steel support column
28 Check
29 Magician's stick
30 A pint, typically, at a blood bank: 2 wds.
32 N.Y.C. subway line
35 Guys' garb
37 Broadcasting
40 "Alfred" composer
41 Sultanate in Borneo
42 Gobs
43 Collar
44 "The Dukes of Hazzard" spinoff

Down

1 Best
2 Eagle's penthouse suite
3 Dr. Herman Tarnower's diet
4 Guesses: abbr.
5 Familiarize
6 Trig. function
7 Knitted sweater fastening down the front
8 "Pulp Fiction" actress Thurman
9 Confederate leader
10 Erstwhile MTV countdown program, initially
16 Freshener scent
19 Persevere: 2 wds.
20 The Magic, on scoreboards
21 Ferdinand, e.g.
23 Light up
25 Classification system for blood
26 Bolivian export
27 Back muscles, to a personal trainer
29 Improvise: 2 wds.
31 Portuguese babies
33 Sought out quickly: 2 wds.
34 Lock of hair
36 Ridge on a textured woven fabric
37 "The ___ Daba Honeymoon"
38 Abbr. on some clothing tags
39 1920 play that introduced the word "robot"

113

Across

1 Unclean

6 Is ___ (probably will): 2 wds.

11 "You can count on me": 2 wds.

12 "The Nutcracker" lead

13 Belly button

14 Sufferer from Hansen's disease

15 "To Tell the Truth" host: 2 wds.

17 Where valuables are kept

18 Main protein in cheese

22 Allergic reaction

25 Give ___ (care): 2 wds.

26 ___ blanche (complete freedom to do as one wishes)

27 Campus quarters

28 Indian tree with multiple trunks

29 Matt of "The Bourne Identity"

31 Supported by both sides

36 Component parts of a skeleton

37 Italian province northwest of Venice

38 Kleenex layers

39 Floor worker

40 Not fresh

41 Syrian president

Down

1 Lindsay Lohan's mother

2 Suffix with poet or paradox

3 Four-star review

4 "Cosmic Dancer" group: 2 wds.

5 Putin's predecessor

6 Roman ___ (novel genre): 2 wds.

7 Commoner in Ancient Rome

8 Woven picture

9 Long haul

10 Rowboat mover

16 Took off quickly

18 Bounder

19 Flurry

20 European island, capital Cagliari

21 John Steed's partner in "The Avengers": 2 wds.

23 Windy City rail inits.

24 It might have a clutch

26 Musical setting for a religious text

28 Staten Island, e.g.: abbr.

30 En ___ (all together)

31 Lock part

32 Horned goddess

33 Musical notes

34 Epithet of Athena

35 L'Étoile du ___, Minnesota's motto

36 Way to measure pulse rates, initially

114

Across

1 Unsettled questions
4 ___ diet: 2 wds.
7 Tic-___ (metronome sound)
10 Joining together
12 "Beautiful job!"
13 1986 Robert Redford/Daryl Hannah movie: 2 wds.
15 Felipe, Jesús and Matty
16 Hard work
17 Evening prayers
19 Not on the job
22 Cold War org.
24 Jack Bauer's org. in "24"
25 Prefix meaning "bad"
27 Chamomile or Earl Grey
28 Marriage site in John 2:1–11
30 Go-carts
32 Work one's lungs
34 "___ Hop" (1958 hit for Danny & the Juniors): 2 wds.
35 Bonnie's partner in crime
39 Noisy quarrel
41 Bray starter
42 Hooch hound
43 Some H.S. students
44 Clothes line?
45 Dark and depressing, as music

Down

1 Actress Fisher of "Wedding Crashers"
2 Get a handle on
3 Palm starch
4 Mustard family flower
5 Direction opposite SSW
6 Showing shock
7 Bear
8 Ornamental shrub of Eurasia
9 "It is" to Pierre
11 Purple shade
14 Singer ___ Stefani
18 "Heidi" author
19 Duke's grp.
20 Alarming person
21 Crescent-shaped windows
23 Grp. founded in Bogotá
26 Caustic comments
29 "Hard Road to Glory" author
31 People who occupied Britain, Spain and Gaul prior to Roman times
33 Capital of Western Australia
34 Oohs and ___
36 "Holy moly!"
37 Dire fate
38 Inner: prefix
40 Miler Sebastian

115

Across

1 Dormitory overseers, initially
4 State capital of North Carolina: abbr.
7 Esq. affixer
8 Previous to, in poesy
9 IV amounts, briefly
12 Singer-songwriter McBride
14 Operated
15 Actress Skye
16 Uninteresting one
17 Awards for Broadway actors
19 Fritter away
20 Dusting cloth
21 "____ the Way It Is" (Celine Dion song)
23 List catchall: abbr.
24 ____ Ben Canaan of "Exodus"
25 Half-brother of Tom Sawyer
28 Abominates
30 Environmental prefix
31 Poplar tree
33 Help-desk staffers, briefly
35 Actress Martha, et al.
36 Louver
37 Barbell abbr.
38 With much sound
41 Chemist's suffix
42 French department and river
43 Yiddish outbursts
44 Wax producer
45 First word of Dante's "Inferno"

Down

1 Pile-driver part
2 One thing ____ time: 2 wds.
3 Food you can pull apart: 2 wds.
4 Put back
5 Composer Thomas
6 Rural sight
9 Representative sample of a larger group: hyph.
10 Vehicle pulled by a horse
11 Old dagger
13 Christmas list item
16 Flying mammal
17 Half of sei
18 Grain for horses
19 What weightwatchers watch
22 Otto I's realm, for short
26 German "I"
27 Windows forerunner
29 Gore and Sharpton
31 Guthrie born at Coney Island
32 Barbara, to friends
34 Federal warning system activated by FEMA
36 French silk
38 Collar
39 Soapmaker's need
40 Fashion inits.

116

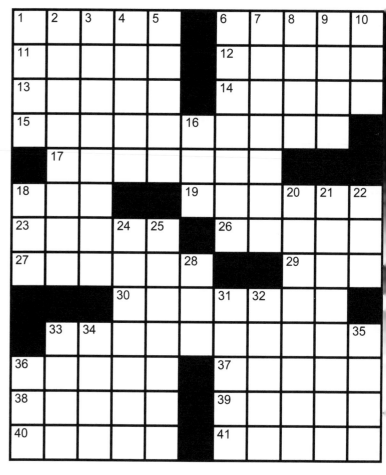

Across

1 Actors' words
6 Hard sell, maybe
11 As a friend in France: 2 wds.
12 Dearest
13 Comparable to a lobster: 2 wds.
14 Oklahoma natives
15 Sideshow attractions: hyph.
17 Household waste
18 Beechbone in "The Lord of the Rings," e.g.
19 Mom's sister
23 Saturn satellite
26 "Girlfriend" boy band
27 Military hero: 2 wds.
29 Strong throw or golf tee
30 Cross-brace that supports a rail on a railway track
33 They can take you up and down mountains
36 Young dog or wolf
37 "Give ___!" ("Try!"): 3 wds.
38 Praises vociferously
39 Philosopher William of ___
40 Deli specification: 2 wds.
41 Nearby things

Down

1 It falls in fall
2 Official emblems
3 Taleteller
4 High guy in Dubai: var.
5 Part of a cassette tape: 2 wds.
6 Smoothbore firearm
7 Illicit Irish whiskeys
8 "___ out?" (poker query): 2 wds.
9 Wide widths, initially
10 Key town in Arthur C. Clarke's "The City and the Stars"
16 Small battery size, initially
18 One of eight Eng. kings
20 Font
21 Krypton, e.g.: 2 wds.
22 Lines from the heart?: inits.
24 With a stuffed-up sound
25 Astronomical event
28 At all times, poetically
31 T S ___, British poet and Nobel prize winner
32 Plunge headlong
33 "Rush Hour" star, 1998
34 Successor
35 A smattering of
36 ___, what, where, when and why

117

Across

1 Alda of "30 Rock"
5 Heron, e.g.
10 Common: prefix
11 Result of a punch
12 End
13 Once in a blue moon
14 Biblical story set to music
16 Alternative to a passing shot
17 Snares
21 Dior creation: hyph.
23 "The Outcasts of Poker Flat" writer Bret
24 Razor brand
25 Part of le printemps
26 Spanish girlfriend
29 Unrefined
31 ___ Galilee: 2 wds.
32 Roadside bomb letters
33 Fire-raiser
37 Neck swelling
40 Precollege, to textbook publishers: hyph.
41 James in many westerns
42 Impressive style
43 "Raw Like Sushi" singer Cherry
44 Fizzy drink

Down

1 Prefix meaning "tip" or "summit"
2 Knowing look
3 "Falcon Crest" actress: 2 wds.
4 ___ Sound, Alaska
5 Apparition
6 The dawn
7 Expire
8 Immigrant's course, initially
9 Foreign leader
11 "I'm so cold!"
15 U.K. award letters
18 Nocturnal mammal with large claws
19 School grps.
20 Uno y dos y tres
21 Desert garments
22 7-Up flavor
27 Col. Sanders' facial hair
28 From the top
29 Labor org.
30 Actress Zellweger and others
34 H.S. veterans
35 Fish usually caught in the winter
36 Louise of "Gilligan's Island"
37 Ramat ___ (Israeli city)
38 Metal in rocks
39 Night spot

118

Across

1 Perp's wristwear
6 Replies to an invitation, briefly
11 Either "Paper Moon" costar
12 Congo, formerly
13 Pear-shaped tropical fruit
14 Actor Lew, Dr. Kildare in nine movies
15 A face that could ___ clock: 2 wds.
17 Mil. ranks
18 Comic Lew
19 Menu word
21 Stasimon, e.g.
22 Plant with waxy, brightly-colored flowers
25 Geom. point
26 Different or potent ending
27 Old trucking watchdog gp.
28 "Why is that?": 2 wds.
30 Atmosphere: prefix
31 What it is in Italy
32 Workplace watchdog, initially
33 "Go ahead!": 2 wds.
35 Arroz con ___, rice and chicken dish
37 Not captured
39 7th-century B.C. Greek city
41 Slalom gold medalist Phil
42 Protagonist in Kafka's "The Metamorphosis"
43 Frostflower
44 City in North Rhine-Westphalia

Down

1 Important part
2 Not comfortable with: 2 wds.
3 Thing not worth serious consideration
4 Party handout
5 Give a hand?
6 Head producer for the Wu-Tang Clan
7 Informs verbally: 2 wds.
8 Cigarette brand that used to sponsor tennis tournaments: 2 wds.
9 ___-à-porter (ready-to-wear)
10 Legis. meeting
16 Handout for tourists: 2 wds.
18 Scotland's Rannoch, Tay or Lomond, e.g.
20 Eye rakishly
22 They sometimes accompany photos, briefly
23 Building used to store frozen water
24 Resort town in the Catskills
29 Kind of mart: hyph.
32 Bulging jars
33 Legislative body of Russia
34 "... carry ___ as if nothing really matters" (Queen lyric)
36 Seine feeder
38 Three times: prefix
40 Woman's counterpart

119

Across

1 Love, Spanish-style
5 Cuatro y cuatro
9 Clean the slate
10 Leafy green
12 Most serious category of crime: 2 wds.
14 Bill accompanier, initially
15 Feel unwell
16 Ode title starter: 2 wds.
17 Lit up
19 Get a load of
22 Spicy Louisiana ham dish
26 D.C. baseball team
27 Duds
28 "Delphine" author Madame de ___
30 Put a stop to
31 "___ Bulba" (fictional Cossack)
33 Rival of UPS and FedEx
36 Grown boy
37 Leg's neighbor
40 Where recipes might be found: 2 wds.
43 Siouan speakers
44 "To be, ___ to be" (Hamlet)
45 Greek salad ingredient
46 No longer mint

Down

1 La Scala showstopper
2 Stallion's mate
3 W.W. II agcy.
4 Labels again
5 Leopardlike cat
6 Bill amt.
7 "Seesaw" singer Beth
8 Cookie often eaten with milk
9 Two in traffic
11 Crime-busters' grp.
13 Tommy's baby brother on "Rugrats"
17 It's no liability
18 Payments for work
19 Ques. response
20 Welcome site
21 ___ snail's pace: 2 wds.
23 Tyrrhenian or Tasman
24 European carrier letters
25 Metallic rock
29 County seat of Dawson County, Texas
30 "Brother, ___ Spare a Dime?" (song): 2 wds.
32 Data compression format letters
33 Seventh-century date
34 Cow's foot
35 "St. Elmo's Fire" actor Rob
37 Tip-top rating: hyph.
38 Large cross
39 Retail estab.
41 Krazy ___ of the comics
42 Apt. features

120

Across

1 Unit of pressure
5 Dishonest sort
10 Cracks sharply
12 Photographer's bath
13 Medical picture-taker: 2 wds.
15 Shrinks' org.
16 Setting for many a joke
17 It follows April in Paris
18 "Cool!": abbr.
19 Immigrant's class, initially
20 Long-distance letters
21 Baby buggy, in Britain
23 Becomes tight or rigid
25 High school exams, for short
27 Rags
30 "Providence" actress Paula
34 Hung. neighbor
35 Ice: Ger.
37 "Platoon" setting, briefly
38 Booker T & the ___
39 Gridiron stats, briefly
40 Oklahoma Indian
41 Tutor's favorite: 2 wds.
44 Like a feeble old woman
45 Île de la Cité locale
46 Cuban-American pianist José
47 Musical with meowing

Down

1 Robin Williams' role in a 1982 movie: inits., 2 wds.
2 Even: 3 wds.
3 Arbor or porch
4 Car tire abbr.
5 Movie actress with aspirations
6 ___ de plume
7 Liquids used to stimulate evacuation
8 Fill with bubbles
9 Banded venomous snakes
11 Kemo ___ (the Lone Ranger)
14 Discarded: 2 wds.
22 Army cops, initially
24 White House advisory group, initially
26 Gets angry
27 Gong: hyph.
28 City south of Salem
29 Tear into
31 Sightlessness
32 Potential
33 Is histrionic
36 Lat., Lith., and Ukr., once
42 151, in Roman numerals
43 Brief time, briefly

121

Across

1 Den denizen
5 Gather up
10 Bundle up
11 Fit for farming
12 Some W.W. II vessels
13 Lady of Spain
14 Dribble
15 Yokohama yes
16 Nicholas ___, dramatist
18 Whitney and Gray
22 Being in operation
25 ___ Maria (liqueur)
26 Provides with a coating
27 Principal movie roles
29 Favored one
30 Value highly
32 Crawl (with)
34 München mister
35 Inflated sense of self-worth
37 Play opener: 2 wds.
40 Japanese automaker
43 Wyndham Lewis novel
44 Intro
45 Beneficiary in law
46 Endures
47 "Miracle" team of 1969

Down

1 OPEC meas.
2 Comfort
3 Serving or used in place of another
4 Give an answer
5 Carpet layer's calculation
6 Rage
7 Three blood groups
8 Camera type, briefly
9 Caribbean or Mediterranean
11 Pale with fright
17 Cheesehead's st.
19 Set of steps
20 Lends a hand
21 Sliding window frame
22 Return request: abbr.
23 "___'s Gold" (1997 movie about a beekeeper)
24 Merriment
28 Printed mistake
31 Crucial moment, militarily: hyph.
33 Intended
36 Some college tests, for short
38 Waste compensation
39 Makes angry
40 Light source
41 "Pull ___ chair!": 2 wds.
42 Wanna-___ (poseurs)

122

Across

1 Out-of-this-world org.
5 "Go away", historically
11 "Oh me!"
12 Moving part in an engine
13 D.C. bigwigs
14 Apologize for sinning
15 Reserve for future use: 2 wds.
17 Tablet
18 Indian bread
22 Approval at sea
24 Toward the back of the boat
26 ET's craft
27 Red Cross supply
28 Negative joiner
29 Chi preceder
30 Give the once-over
31 Bunion's place
32 Legend on the ice
33 Database command
35 Light bulb's home
37 Situated on a higher floor
41 Threw with force
44 Elation
45 Kind of rhododendron
46 Condition
47 Opportune
48 Element element

Down

1 Rest periods
2 Hand lotion additive
3 Potassium nitrate
4 Brazilian palm
5 Date for playing practical jokes: 3 wds.
6 Competed
7 Skier's mecca
8 Shoshonean language
9 Prefix for profit
10 Atlanta-based station
16 Editorial bias
19 Device that keeps a plane on a set course
20 Many miles away
21 Black, as la nuit
22 Cards quartet
23 Toy with a string: hyph.
25 Halloween option
34 Gown fabric
36 Lava, while underground
38 Rind
39 Change the decor
40 Give the appearance of
41 Stetson, e.g.
42 Compact submachine gun
43 St. Louis pro

123

Across

1 Takeoff and landing overseers, initially
4 A mah-jongg tile
7 Goat's groan
10 Wall St. type
11 Certain fraternity chapter
12 Elmer, to Bugs
13 Catalog anew
15 Boy's name in a Johnny Cash title
16 False front
17 Rains in pellets
19 Serve in the capacity of: 2 wds.
21 Jews born in Israel
24 Mailing courtesies, initially
28 Disney mermaid
29 Native New Zealander
30 Marriage site in John 2:1
31 Fashions
32 1953 Alan Ladd movie
34 Of a nation
37 Dudley Do-Right's org.
41 Women's ___
42 Cowboy using a rope
44 Vicksburg soldier, shortly
45 Grant-giving agency, initially
46 Spelling or quilting event
47 Mediterranean isl.
48 Criminal charge
49 1960s grp.

Down

1 Golden ager's org.
2 Early smartphone
3 U.K. honorees
4 "Wanna ___?"
5 They produce mushroom clouds, briefly: 2 wds.
6 "The Jeffersons" actress Gibbs
7 Gds.
8 August, in Amiens
9 Poker "bullets"
14 Countries of southwestern Asia: 2 wds.
18 Trying people?
20 Ariz. neighbor
21 Anatomic pouch
22 Celestial altar
23 Hopper
25 Big ISP
26 Milton's "before"
27 Certain sibling, affectionately
29 Mont Blanc, for short
31 Tea brand
33 More healthy
34 Certain cameras: inits.
35 "___ Yellow Ribbon Round the Ole Oak Tree" (song by Dawn featuring Tony Orlando): 2 wds.
36 Short form, for short
38 Woody parts of corn ears
39 Reward, old style
40 CEO, often: abbr.
43 Easy mark

124

Across

1 Aleutian island
5 ____ Clements, bluegrass and country musician
11 Big name in faucets
12 "Psst!" follower: 2 wds.
13 Quantities: abbr.
14 10 of them make a thou: hyph.
15 Take care of: 2 wds.
17 1960s do
18 Murder suspect in "Lohengrin"
22 Crying: 2 wds.
25 Stick in the water
26 Billy ____ Williams
27 Never abroad
28 151, to Caesar
29 "Can't Help Lovin' ____ Man" (Ella Fitzgerald)
30 Vulture's dinner?
32 Pitcher Hershiser
34 Woman's net cap, historically
35 Plane, e.g.
39 Campfire brand
42 "Shades of Blue" actress de Matteo
43 Hooks on which a door turns
44 King of Shakespeare
45 Leftover
46 Bring home the bacon

Down

1 Part of a Latin trio
2 Big book
3 Private conversation: hyph.
4 Risky
5 Brit. military award: 2 wds.
6 "Green Gables" girl
7 Coast
8 TV ____
9 "You ____ My Destiny"
10 In medias ____
16 Swiss currency
19 Your region: 2 wds.
20 "Do the Right Thing" setting
21 Onassis and Emanuel
22 "____ Anything" ("Oliver!" song): 2 wds.
23 Come up to
24 Glacial ice formation
31 Turn, as milk
33 The "L" of XXL
36 ____ Sastre, Aurora in "The Lost City"
37 Cause of shaking and quaking
38 Glacier-formed lake
39 "Ain't ____ Sweet"
40 They get you into a concert, casually
41 Abbr. at the bottom of a letter

125

Across

1 Baby's bed
5 Golf great Sam
10 Put light on
11 Arterial vessel
12 Armored vehicles
13 Michael of R.E.M.
14 Deprive of real estate
16 ____ Fugard, playwright who works include "Blood Knot"
17 Big name in mapmaking
20 "Hubba hubba!": 3 wds.
24 Little battery letters
25 Hosp. employee
26 Beaver's structure
27 Prescence of harmful bacteria in tissues
29 Church service
30 Eater of eucalyptus leaves
32 Loud
37 "____ nearly there yet?": 2 wds.
38 1,000 kilograms
39 "Psycho" motel
40 Foofaraws: hyph.
41 Consumers
42 Jug handle, in archeology

Down

1 Milky spiced tea
2 Howard and Brown
3 Stamp rejuvenator: 2 wds.
4 Inebriate
5 Big name in hairstyling
6 Kind of motel, slangily
7 Discordia's Greek counterpart
8 Biol. energy sources
9 "Hawaii Five-0" actor, Daniel ____ Kim
10 Basic version: abbr.
15 Patronizes (a store): 2 wds.
17 ____ Tafari (Haile Selassie)
18 Org. for dentists
19 Catch a few Zs
21 Cavity fillers' org.
22 "Viva ____ Vegas"
23 Forenoons, initially
25 Certain female wild cat
28 Spit for holding meat in place
29 Leave on an island
31 "Whole ____ Love" (Led Zeppelin song)
32 Mrs.'s counterparts, in Mexico
33 French head
34 Swing voters: abbr.
35 Forest ox
36 Sega rival, for short
37 "Aladdin" monkey

126

Across

1 Sheds tears
6 Difficult question
11 Reddish brown
12 Province of central Spain
13 Community feeling
14 Bowling alley button
15 Cooking appliance with a rotating spit
17 Knotting
18 Hung around
21 First name in Persian poetry
25 Call for help, initially
26 But, to Brutus
28 Way to shoot down a plane, initially
29 Fly like an eagle
31 Embroidery cloth
33 Mindful (of)
35 Flavor sensation remaining in the mouth
40 Conductor Sir Georg
41 Inexperienced
42 Some Harvard students, briefly: 2 wds.
43 Absolute
44 Feet, in old Rome
45 Cacophonous

Down

1 Blacken
2 Musical equipment company
3 Monogram part: abbr.
4 Being
5 Gives one's assent: 2 wds.
6 (or), briefly
7 Exceed
8 Mexican's assent: 2 wds.
9 Gen. Robt. ___: 2 wds.
10 Alley denizen
16 Vehicle attached to a motorcycle
18 Leaky tire sound
19 Likewise
20 Simile's middle: 2 wds.
22 Dallas cager, briefly
23 Little battery size, initially
24 Apt. ad stat
27 Tranquilizer's tool: 2 wds.
30 Unnerve
32 Close by: 2 wds.
34 Dam on the Coosa River
35 Rave rating: hyph.
36 Ran away quickly
37 "Are we alone?" prog.
38 Caddie's bagful
39 "Just you wait, ___ 'iggins…"
40 Dipper's bread

127

Across

1 "This feels good!"
4 Prefix with puncture
7 Dismiss derisively: 2 wds.
9 Gordon Brown and David Cameron, briefly
12 First name in dance
13 ___ Claire, Wis.
14 "Revenge" getter of film
15 Beat
17 French funnyman Jacques
19 Fair-hiring letters
20 Leaves alone: 2 wds.
22 "River ___ Return" movie starring Mitchum and Monroe: 2 wds.
24 ___ y plata
25 Wall St. worker
27 Friction reducer
28 Homer Simpson shouts
30 New Guinea native
32 Leaves in a bag
33 "___ Old Cowhand from the Rio Grande": 2 wds.
34 Meaningful talk
36 Classic Army bomber plane: 2 wds.
39 To the other side: abbr.
40 Gourmet cook's condiment: 2 wds.
42 Bunting tool
43 Combat pilots' missions
44 Bibliophilic suffix
45 Arrest

Down

1 Q ___ "queen": 2 wds.
2 Addie's husband in "As I Lay Dying"
3 Intimate talk in private: hyph.
4 Nigerian native
5 Bird trained to take messages: 2 wds.
6 Salt Lake City's state
8 Collections of Old Norse poems
9 World-renowned clarinetist from New Orleans: 2 wds.
10 Evergreen shrub
11 Bottom line
16 River in Somerset, England
18 Not yet specified, briefly
20 Ben Gurion Airport's former name
21 1992 Madonna album
23 Canadian TV channel, initially
26 "Kapow!"
29 Mineo of "Exodus"
31 Big name in brewing
34 Smidge
35 Bones, anatomically
37 Home of Zeno
38 Crash investigating agcy.
41 Rome's ___ Pacis

128

Across

1 Noncom ranks
5 1205, to Caesar
9 Israeli airline: 2 wds.
10 Barcelona boat
11 Kitchen devices: 2 wds.
13 Small songbird
14 Caesar: "___ iacta est" ("The die is cast")
15 Indian dignitary: var.
17 Native of Media
21 Mild, as weather
23 Papa
24 Not worth ___ of beans: 2 wds.
26 Faulty
28 Disney frame
29 Draw a bead on: 2 wds.
31 Out of port
33 Substance diffused in the air
35 Lackluster
37 Greek letter
39 Enthronement
42 Second U.S. president
43 Classic Welles role
44 "That Should ___" (Justin Bieber song): 2 wds.
45 Olive-tree genus

Down

1 Denomination
2 Natural ability
3 In a smooth singing style
4 ___-pitch softball
5 Lion's pride
6 Elite group
7 "Bad Moon Rising" band, briefly
8 "___ in Victor": 2 wds.
10 Port at the mouth of the Amazon
12 Rice dish made with saffron
16 Ending with infer or inter
18 Newspaper opinion column
19 Court people, for short
20 Hardy and Asner
22 Big piano maker
24 In this location: Span.
25 "___ My Girl" (1987 film)
27 Street finder
30 Several tsars
32 The "A" in James A. Garfield
34 French wine region
36 Togo's capital
38 Ready for service: hyph.
39 Taxi
40 Flowery verse
41 W.B.A. decision

129

Across

1 Make well
5 Red ___ (Ferrara candy brand)
9 Train track bar: hyph.
11 Pale shades of beige
13 Passerine bird
14 Chiquis Rivera album of 2015
15 D.D.E.'s command
16 Dozes: 2 wds.
18 Shaft of light
20 South Carolina's ___ Dee River
21 Conductor Georg
22 Part of a footnote abbr.
23 Suggest
25 Gray
27 Highlands negative
28 ___ miss (haphazardly): 2 wds.
30 Up to, informally
31 Ancient region of Italy
34 Poorly constructed: hyph.
36 "Lost" setting: abbr.
37 Video game designer Sid
38 Mattress cover
40 "Ninotchka" director Lubitsch
41 Eastern wrap: var.
42 Campus orgs.
43 Bygone leader

Down

1 Busy places
2 Verdi aria sung by Renato: 2 wds.
3 TV executive producer: 2 wds.
4 Make up something
5 Female principal of a school
6 Folk singer Phil
7 Vehicles for transporting soldiers: 2 wds.
8 Glut, excess
10 "Sgt. Pepper's ___ Club Band": 2 wds.
12 Security, sanctuary
17 Cracklin' ___ Bran (Kellogg's cereal)
19 Neighbor of Arg. and Parag.
23 Sooner or later: 2 wds.
24 Letter senders
26 "Skip to My ___"
29 "___ be nice if ..."
32 "___ Darkness" (Johnny Cash song): 3 wds.
33 Redo a tuxedo
35 Arizona city
39 Pillbox, e.g.

130

Across

1 Helps
5 Make a difference to
11 Young horse
12 Local ruler
13 Architectural pier
14 Couch potatoes' fixations: 2 wds.
15 Bring back to a former condition
17 Have
22 Position of a person in society
26 Cat: Sp.
27 Dances at Jewish weddings
28 "I do ___ proud man …" ("Troilus and Cressida"): 2 wds.
29 Basic util.
30 Lazy and black-eyed
31 Miniature racer: 2 wds.
33 Pirate's sword
38 Old Ford: 2 wds.
42 Castle entrance, perhaps
43 Get there
44 Org. that sues pirates
45 Printing character: ‡
46 "With God ___ witness": 2 wds.

Down

1 At the horizon
2 Skye of "River's Edge"
3 Some cassettes, briefly
4 Narrow, thin strip
5 Team in the largest city in Texas
6 Top picks, in slang
7 Henry and McHenry: abbr.
8 Poetic word for "before"
9 Dude
10 Defaces with rolls?: abbr.
16 Magnum follower
18 Campus orgs.
19 "___ Bowl of Tea" (Wayne Wang movie): 2 wds.
20 British gun
21 Provided that: 2 wds.
22 Cows and sows
23 Going rate?
24 Of Mars (comb. form)
25 Delicacy
28 In pain
30 Fries quickly in a little hot fat
32 256, to a Roman
34 "Tomb Raider" protagonist Croft
35 Onassis and Emanuel
36 Cheat
37 Two-wheeled carriage, colloquially
38 Daft
39 "… ___ quit!": 2 wds.
40 Dr. of rap
41 Autobahn hazard

131

Across

1 Giant syllable
4 Supermarket franchise letters
7 Agency of the Department of Justice, initially
10 Mag. workers
11 Hesitant sounds
12 Sch. in Kingston
13 Bitty bite
14 Tapping sound: hyph.
16 "Cannery Row" character
18 Skepticism
19 Quell
21 Haves and have-___
23 Explorer Sport ___ (Ford SUV)
24 Narrative
25 School grouping in some states, initially
27 "___ Poetica"
29 Abbr. after a name
30 Two in middle?
32 Rubber-stamped
34 Small river fish
35 Letters from Greece
38 Hangs around
40 Bits and pieces
41 Fast delivery method
43 Game played with "It"
44 Beat
45 Pig ___ poke: 2 wds.
46 "___ et labora" (pray and work)
47 T or F, on exams: abbr.
48 T-shirt sizes: abbr.
49 Sib.

Down

1 Wards (off)
2 Bonehead
3 Feeling of loyalty shared by members of a group: 3 wds.
4 Suffix with front
5 Place where a road and railroad meet: 2 wds.
6 Anent: 2 wds.
7 Engine at the back of a small boat: 2 wds.
8 Childish talk
9 River islet
15 Father's sister
17 Botswana's continent, briefly
20 When doubled, a yellow Teletubby
22 Gelled
25 "The Tonight Show" announcer Hall
26 Large, ocean-dwelling mammal
28 Get towed, maybe
31 A-line line
33 Latin abbrs.
36 To love, Italian style
37 George of "Just Shoot Me"
39 Get a terrible grade on
41 ___ premium: 2 wds.
42 ___ Tunas, Cuba

132

Across

1. Tight-fitting hats
5. Fix, as a medical condition
9. Wings, anatomically
10. Words at the start of a countdown: 2 wds.
12. With good intentions: hyph.
14. One who advocates change
15. Go wild: 2 wds.
17. Anti-flooding device
20. "I'm just ___!"
22. Donkeys in Dijon
23. Ankle bones
24. Wrecks
26. "Good Times" star Esther
27. Arsonist
29. Moved swiftly and uncontrollably
32. Considered carefully and at length
35. Start, date-wise: 2 wds.
36. Wrinkly-faced dogs
37. "James Dean: a Biography" author William
38. Blow off steam?

Down

1. Cornfield sound
2. Yankee or Angel, for short
3. Not deep in color
4. A refraining from excess: hyph.
5. Early motion-picture projector
6. Tiger Paw tire maker
7. Take part in a race
8. Perry Mason creator's monogram

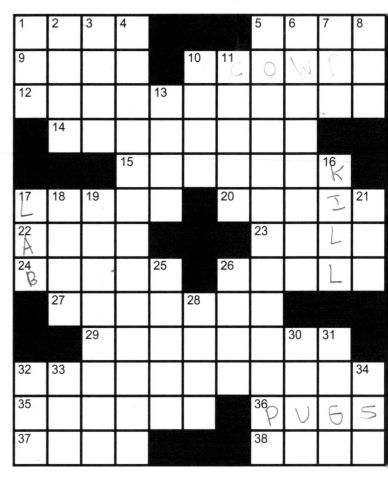

10. Cousin of a gull
11. ___ boy
13. Grimace of discontent
16. Put to death
17. Biol. class setting
18. Sufficient, informally
19. Fluid-filled cysts
21. Never, in Nürnberg
25. ___-Croat
26. Contrite one
28. "___ there, done that!"
30. Decorative case
31. Colleges award them: abbr.
32. Driver's license info, for short
33. It tests the water, initially
34. Community studies deg.

133

Across

1 Southeastern Conf. team
5 "Who Will Answer?" singer: 2 wds.
11 Turkish bigwigs
12 Compels
13 Sots' spots
14 Not worth doing
15 1997 U.S. Open winner
16 Univ. grants
17 "Vega$" star Robert
19 Ring org.
22 Meal
24 Shakespeare, for one
25 Not repressed
27 Long bath
28 "Unfamiliar Fishes" author Sarah
29 Subject for immigrants, initially
30 Popeye's creator
31 Kind of column
32 Org. for golfers
35 Calm down
38 Not bad at all
39 Free-for-all
40 Jordan's Queen ___ Airport
41 Narrow boats
42 Express ride

Down

1 Sweetie pie
2 "___ in Calico" (1946 song): 2 wds.
3 Pouched mammal
4 Dodo
5 Success
6 Bread before cooking
7 Aesthetic practices
8 Sprint rival, once: inits.
9 Wet wriggler
10 Amsterdam to Rome dir.
16 Plate
18 General or corporal
19 Game played in a pool
20 "Jacques ___ is Alive and Well…"
21 Extra: abbr.
22 Dodge
23 Baseball's Slaughter
24 Japanese short-necked lute
26 Wetlands
30 Bristles
31 Dinner Bell?
33 Enter: 2 wds.
34 "There will come ___…": 2 wds.
35 NCO rank
36 Mesozoic or Cenozoic
37 Newsman Rather
38 Generation separator

134

Across

1 "___ here long?"
5 Shivering fits
10 Genetic strands, initially
11 Trade by exchange
13 Murder, especially a socially prominent person
15 Fellow
16 Bic or Mont Blanc, e.g.
17 Degree from RISD
18 Deck figure
20 Sportscaster Cross
21 Some computer monitors, initially
23 Born, in bios
24 ___ Ababa
27 What a plant often grows from: 2 wds.
29 "Mamma ___!"
30 Alpine reply?
32 Delt. neighbor
33 Illuminated naturally
37 "Baudolino" author
38 Abbr. on some sheet music
39 ___Kosh B'gosh (clothing brand)
40 Cross brace on a track: 2 wds.
43 Favor
44 Japanese professional golfer, ___ Aoki
45 Amateurs
46 Circus crowd's sounds

Down

1 Acts the blowhard
2 Come to pass
3 Class that doesn't require much studying: 2 wds.
4 Codebreaking arm of govt.
5 Missing, as from class
6 Capital ___
7 Coffee brewer
8 Cotton fabric
9 Release: 2 wds.
12 Plundered
14 Meager
19 Former Sprint competitor, initially
22 Big African desert
24 Current amount
25 Molded, as metal
26 Robbery by a gang
28 ___ sauce
31 Computer devices: hyph.
34 "___ luck!" ("Knock 'em dead!")
35 1990 NBA Finals MVP ___ Thomas
36 TV's Huxtable and Kojak, for two
38 Mars: prefix
41 Celtic Neptune
42 Day: Sp.

135

Across

1 Bumbling people
5 Cartoonist Addams
9 2006 Olympics host
11 Distressed
13 Ryan of "The Beverly Hillbillies"
14 "___ vires" (within the legal power of)
15 One of five on a foot
16 Forenoons, initially
18 Suffix with Jacob
19 "___: Deadliest Roads" (reality TV series)
20 French flower
21 "World of Warcraft", e.g.
22 Mort the comedian
24 Not belonging to anybody: 2 wds.
26 "Desperately Seeking Susan" star Arquette
28 Meteorologist's line
30 Not much at all: 2 wds.
33 Morning moisture
34 They pull in pushers, initially
36 Sussex suffix
37 One-time domestic flight co.
38 To the ___ power
39 Radio org.
40 "The Brady Bunch" housekeeper
42 Put riders on, say
44 "Peanuts" boy
45 Prove to be mistaken
46 Bus. card data
47 Actress Cannon

Down

1 Inflammation of the ear
2 Greek goddess of the dawn
3 It's 15 feet from the hoop, in basketball: 3 wds.
4 Fall from grace
5 Artillery ammunition vehicle
6 Hua ___ (Thai beach resort)
7 As another possibility
8 Colorful wrap
10 Broten of hockey fame
12 Euphemistic expletives
17 Slender tower with balconies
23 High ball
25 "Put ___ Happy Face": 2 wds.
27 Sorrow
28 Archetype
29 "___ With a Kiss" (Britney Spears song): 2 wds.
31 Tone deafness
32 Muffle
35 Captain of the Pequod
41 ___-de-sac
43 Kind of school or student, for short

136

Across

1 Attain

6 / mark

11 "Be-Bop-___" (1956 Gene Vincent hit): hyph.

12 Shrewd

13 Put off, as a potential threat

14 Hall of Famer Sandberg et al.

15 Sigmund's "ego"

16 Grant-giving agency, initially

18 Prefix for logical

19 ___ Z: 2 wds.

20 Glove compartment item

21 BBC rival

22 "Cheers" regular

24 Falling-out

26 Chinese secret society

28 Popular Mexican palm-like plant

31 They have phalanges

33 It's available in bars

34 Arthur of "The Golden Girls"

36 Ms. ___-Man (video game)

38 Tikkanen of hockey

39 Genre of popular music, initially

40 Subject in a sem. or a ser.

41 Attention-getter

42 Cartoon art

44 Second part of a stage production: 2 wds.

46 Clothes lines?

47 Live on a minimum salary

48 Underwear brand

49 "Calvin and Hobbes" girl

Down

1 Beaming

2 Citizen who has the right to vote

3 Expecting unquestioning obedience

4 A.L. Central city

5 Kingsley film of 1985

6 Scooby's cartoon nephew

7 Not of the cloth

8 Words on a one-dollar bill: 2 wds.

9 Hägar's pooch

10 Lucky Dragon Tea

17 Court figs.

23 ___ tse-Tung

25 Vienna's country: abbr.

27 Sadden

29 The "Jackie Look" designer Oleg

30 Mineral used in fertilizers

32 Freelancer's enc.

34 Offensively bold

35 Word form of "nine"

37 Reunion group

43 Mrs., in Montmartre

45 Jack Bauer's org. in "24"

137

Across

1 Some movie theaters, initially
5 Safety org.
9 "___ With a View": 2 wds.
10 Eddie's "Coming to America" role
12 Country, capital Riyadh: 2 wds.
14 Metric units: abbr.
15 Light opener
16 Like a lot of clues in this puzzle: abbr.
17 South American three-toed sloths
18 Remote control device
20 Fraction of a min.: 2 wds.
22 Put right
23 Broadway phantom's haunt
25 Fasten with a pop: 2 wds.
28 1998 Wimbledon winner Novotna
32 Camp shelter securer: 2 wds.
34 Celtic sea god
35 "NCIS" villain ___ Haswari
36 Big Ten Conference sch.
37 Immigrant's study, initially
38 Sympathize
41 1971 Jane Fonda film
42 MS. enclosures
43 Theories
44 ___ record: 2 wds.

Down

1 Popular fragrance
2 Foamy hairstyling preparation
3 Atlantic food fish
4 John who played Slim Sherman on "Laramie"
5 Sailor
6 Letters before an alias
7 Knock down
8 Heated up, like a frozen windshield
9 Happy ___ be: 2 wds.
11 Saybrooke of "One Life to Live"
13 Knowledge
19 Key of Pachelbel's Canon: abbr., 2 wds.
21 Egyptian Christian
24 Showy field flowers
25 Breakfast order
26 ___ oil (cologne ingredient)
27 Bad blood
29 Orioles' and Red Sox's group: 2 wds.
30 Fuze rival
31 Where Van Gogh painted "Sunflowers"
33 "You'll never ___!"
39 "Lou Grant" production co.
40 ___ Dawn Chong of "Commando"

138

Across

1 Sit in the tub
5 Signs of healing
10 TV actress Georgia
12 Take ___ (travel): 2 wds.
13 Relating to the land
15 Peg used in golf
16 Prefix with grammatical
17 Resembling: 2 wds.
18 Father of Odysseus
20 Vermont neighbor, initially
21 "Das Rheingold" goddess
22 Over
24 ___ Rose (Axis Sally's counterpart)
26 Fortress, stronghold
29 New years in Vietnam
33 Baseball card stat.
34 Working parents' need: 2 wds.
36 Neighbor of Bol. and Para.
37 Abilene to San Antonio dir.
38 Prefix with drome
39 Self-publishing alternative: 2 wds.
42 Hacienda brick
43 Cook lightly in a pan
44 Pavarotti, e.g.
45 Ltr. addenda

Down

1 Resolve
2 "In ___ and out the other": 2 wds.
3 Consented
4 Plunk starter?
5 Fulfill requirements
6 Municipal bldg.
7 French satellite-launching rocket
8 Onion-topped bread rolls
9 Spatter in small drops
11 Internet writing system with unconventional spelling
14 Illicit drinking club
19 "Infestation" rock group
23 Mil. prep. course
25 Senior person
26 Necktie alternative
27 Rub down
28 Enlist: 2 wds.
30 Relax: 2 wds.
31 Assignations
32 Has a hunch
35 Slangy assents
40 Nigerian native
41 Light knock

139

Across

1 Intensified, as sound, briefly
6 Atty.-wannabe's exam
10 Czech composer Antonín
12 Calendar abbr.
13 Actress Langtry
14 Three, to a German
15 Hollers
17 Physics unit
18 Antiquity, once
20 Swedish seaport on the Baltic
22 Envelope closer
24 Bested
27 Less rude
29 "I've ___ for music": 2 wds.
30 Suffers a bad defeat, slangily: 2 wds.
32 "Hairspray" mom
33 "Golden ___" (David Bowie song)
35 Elko-to-Reno dir.
36 Cable alternative, initially
38 Electronic instrument, briefly
40 Perched upon
42 Conduits for carrying off waste products
45 Old French coins
46 Agreement between nations
47 Possesses, in the Bible
48 Heads in Paris

Down

1 Org. founded in 1913 by B'nai B'rith
2 1006, in old Rome
3 Having more than the usual number of fingers or toes
4 ___ Wilson, Aussie novelist
5 Every 24 hours
6 Inc., abroad
7 Classic breakfast cereal: 2 wds.
8 Teacher of Heifetz
9 Math branch: abbr.
11 "Scrubs" chief of medicine
16 Shock momentarily, as with news
18 Medieval laborer
19 Luke's "Star Wars" twin
21 Stick ___ in the water: 2 wds.
23 Literally, "injured"
25 Fleming and Ziering
26 No-win situation
28 Inlets
31 Romantic rendezvous
34 Dog in the funnies
36 Pizazz
37 Ancient gathering place
39 Affectedly dainty or refined
41 S.F. hours
43 A.A.A. recommendation: abbr.
44 Part of CBS: abbr.

140

Across

1 Mugger stopper
5 World Golf Hall of Famer Mark
11 Down with, in Dieppe: 2 wds.
12 James ___, Civil rights leader
13 Greek consonants
14 Donnybrook
15 Blood poisoning
17 Mideast capital: var.
18 Two-time U.S. Open champion
22 Carafe size
23 Mint department: abbr.
24 Biblical high priest
25 Feature with a high elev.
26 Town in Tennessee
29 School events
31 Church council
32 "24 Hours from Tulsa" singer Pitney
33 Sounds
35 Unfounded rumor
38 Breed
41 "The Ice Storm" director: 2 wds.
42 Zeno's home
43 Covered in trees
44 The Amish, e.g.

Down

1 "Welcome" site?
2 Grp. for a defensive person?
3 Bringing about of an effect
4 Ancient ascetic
5 Trade-___ (pluses and minuses)
6 Hudson River Valley college
7 Writing remover
8 Car co. bought by Chrysler
9 Blakey of "Birth Day Live!"
10 ___ longa, vita brevis
16 Average
17 Foolish
19 Fish restaurant dish: 2 wds.
20 Words Alice read on a cake: 2 wds.
21 Phisher's acquisitions, for short
22 Refuse
27 Presidential first name
28 "Call of the Flesh" costar Renée
29 Some film ratings, initially
30 ___ Peanut Butter Cups
34 Picked out of a lineup, briefly
35 Crow comment
36 Enero through Diciembre
37 Vietnam's ___ Dinh Diem
39 VCR remote button, briefly
40 Sylvester, to Tweety

141

Across

1 Abbr. on a French envelope
4 Geom. solid
7 Owns
10 Wagner's "___ fliegende Holländer"
11 Ancient cross
12 Suffix with green or rook
13 One of many at LaGuardia: 2 wds.
16 Involuntary quivering movement
17 "Guys and Dolls" writer: 2 wds.
22 Run off to the chapel
23 Vanzetti's partner in anarchy
24 Pierre Corneille play: "Le ___"
25 Dejected
26 Corroded: 2 wds.
29 Subject of the Shepard Fairey poster "Hope"
31 Paternoster: 2 wds.
33 Fall in Britain
34 Question thoroughly
39 Federation of trade unions, initially
40 Atmospheric prefix
41 Fix, as an election
42 Suffix with puppet or profit
43 Baseball Hall-of-Famer ___ Wee Reese
44 Letters between L and P

Down

1 Labor Day telethon org., once
2 "Tell ___ Was Dreaming" (Travis Tritt song): 2 wds.
3 Make a blunder
4 "Tristram Shandy" author
5 Kitchen gizmo
6 Middle Eastern hors d'oeuvre
7 Orator nicknamed the "Great Compromiser": 2 wds.
8 Constellation near Norma
9 Word div.
14 Car roof feature: hyph.
15 Island close to Mull
17 Design for transfer onto glass, etc.
18 Samuel on the Supreme Court
19 Internet forum monitor
20 "___ All Ye Faithful": 2 wds.
21 "I Dreamed There Was ___" (Eagles instrumental): 2 wds.
27 Together, on a score: 2 wds.
28 Shoe design: hyph.
29 At least: 2 wds.
30 Close violently (as a door)
32 Fruit or vegetable pulp
34 Cooler
35 Never, in Nuremberg
36 Shirt-sleeve filler
37 Pewter metal
38 It may get bruised

142

Across

1 French soul
4 Follower of Bacchus in Ancient Greece
7 Hollywood studio that released "King Kong" and "Citizen Kane", initially
10 Bolstering
11 Conform strictly
12 Rikki-tikki-___
13 ___ number (product identifier)
15 "Would you like ___?" (waitress' question): 2 wds.
17 Rest stop, once
18 Application datum letters
19 Lose consciousness: 2 wds.
22 Ballroom dance: hyph.
24 Trip
26 Honorary law degree, initially
29 Cross inscription, for short
30 Certain photographs: hyph.
32 Casually cheerful
35 "The sign of extra service" sloganeer
36 Federal warning system, initially
37 British blue-bloods: abbr.
39 Orchestra: abbr.
40 Poetic foot
41 Magazine no.

Down

1 Losing it will make a maid mad
2 Operates (a piece of equipment)
3 Brink
4 Superior ladies
5 Recklessness in politics or foreign affairs
6 ___ chief (mag. boss): 2 wds.
7 Official name for a "nose job"
8 Neo's portrayer in "The Matrix"
9 Just-hatched hooter
10 Grps. concerned with class struggle?
14 Acclivity
16 At the time of
20 "Peer Gynt" character
21 "Kilroy Was Here" band, or a mythical river
23 Habeas corpus, e.g.
24 Agrees
25 Decoration fixed to the surface of something else
27 Popular disinfectant
28 Brit. decorations
31 Leftovers
33 "___ known then…": 2 wds.
34 Radio and Disco, e.g.
38 Suffix for graph or gymnast

143

Across

1 Carter Pewterschmidt's wife on "Family Guy"
5 Trousers for casual wear
11 Work without ___: 2 wds.
12 Pitcher Fingers or pitcher Sheldon
13 African country: 2 wds.
15 Bout of indulgence
16 Like fine wine
17 Cut-price events
20 Be disrespectful to
23 Capital of Kazakhstan
27 Highest heart or spade
28 Freq. performer at Tanglewood
29 MSN competitor
30 Argentine grassland
32 Not common
33 ___ Gay (W.W. II plane)
35 Lincoln and Burrows
38 "Boy, Did ___ Wrong Number!" (Bob Hope movie): 3 wds.
42 Feeling or manifesting veneration
45 Ab ___ (from the beginning)
46 Ciara song of 2005
47 Prepares clams, perhaps
48 Liza Minelli's former husband David

Down

1 Low pitch
2 "There's ___ in the air": 2 wds.
3 Oktoberfest serving
4 Tension
5 Mexican Mrs.
6 "That's hilarious," online
7 Blue Jays' and Rays' group: 2 wds.
8 Basin blocker
9 Cattle, poetically
10 Progeny
14 Actor Stephen
18 Catch with a rope
19 That, to Tomás
20 Plant production
21 Here, in Mexico
22 Two qtrs.
24 Bumper sticker letters
25 Neither here ___ there
26 Ginger ___
28 Declare off-limits
31 Currency replaced by the euro
32 Disheveled
34 Civil Rights Memorial designer
35 Onassis and Emanuel
36 Predisposition
37 "A Letter for ___" (1945 film)
39 Deutsche article
40 Small amounts
41 Came to rest
43 Crater's edge
44 Aurora, to the Greeks

144

Across

1 Ignoring: 2 wds.
7 Four-year coll. deg.
10 Lender who charges too much interest
11 Sevillan shouts
12 "You don't think I'll do it, do you?": 2 wds.
13 MasterCard alternative
14 Disorder characterized by convulsions
16 Take into account
19 From scratch
20 Slow movement, in music
24 Producing strong, clear mental images
26 ____ squash
27 Blood issue
29 ____ erectus
30 Almond confection
32 Delicate and intricate ornamentation
35 Have ____ (be connected): 2 wds.
36 Glass eels
40 Carol
41 Carol starter
42 Man-mouse link: 2 wds.
43 Least cooked

Down

1 Firecracker that doesn't go off
2 Demonstrative pronombre
3 Sound-related prefix
4 Like a motile marine animal: hyph.
5 Presto and vivace
6 "When it says ____, it's All Righta" co.: hyph.
7 Radar image
8 "____, You Is My Woman Now" (Gerswin song)
9 Have ____ in: 2 wds.
11 One who performs better than expected
15 Lover of Zeus
16 Spanish wine similar to champagne
17 Johnny Bristol song: "Hang ____ There Baby": 2 wds.
18 Campbell of "House of Cards"
21 Mawkish sentiment
22 "The Joy of Cooking" author Rombauer
23 "____, U of K" (fight song at the University of Kentucky): 2 wds.
25 Cater-cornered: abbr.
28 Unpaid debt
31 Mrs. F. Scott Fitzgerald
32 Burkina ____
33 "____ out?": 2 wds
34 Director Wertmüller
37 Ending for Canton or Nepal
38 Some turns on the road: abbr.
39 Fully prepared

145

Across

1 Plant stalks
6 Frantic
10 Sine reciprocal, briefly
11 Platte River tribe
13 Suitable and fitting
15 1959 hit for The Kingston Trio
16 Where Mork and Mindy honeymooned
17 Devotee
18 Roman house gods
20 Frozen water in Germany
21 Words before "uproar" or "instant": 2 wds.
22 Embrace lovingly
24 Baloney
26 Crumbling of a tooth
29 Annapolis inits.
33 Fruity drink
34 Letters sent by plane
36 Japanese computer company, shortly
37 Law in France
38 Former long-distance phone letters
39 Set of questions evaluating knowledge
42 Where people nosh
43 Author Zora ____ Hurston
44 Edible bivalve mollusk
45 Busts broncos

Down

1 Seafood entree
2 Hit list: 2 wds.
3 Spain in Spain
4 Eau naturelle?
5 Hightail it
6 Builds, as an appetite: 2 wds.
7 "Lord, is ____?": Matthew: 2 wds.
8 Lollygagged
9 Particular
12 Feel in one's bones
14 Exactness, accuracy
19 Con
23 "Te ____" (hymn)
25 Sober outlook
26 Like some chairs
27 Concept pitcher, shortly: 2 wds.
28 Bring back to mind
30 "Green Eggs and Ham" character: hyph.
31 "Grace of Monaco" star Kidman
32 Some dresses: hyph.
35 Pleasingly mirthful
40 Soccer standout Hamm
41 Leaves in a cup

146

Across

1 Great quantity

6 City, informally

9 Woke up after passing out: 2 wds.

11 Have ___ in one's bonnet: 2 wds.

12 Online newsgroup system

13 "Welcome" sights

14 Forbidden: var.

15 Filbert

17 ___ Bator, Mongolia

18 Prince album "___ the Times": 2 wds.

19 Approx. camera flash duration: 2 wds.

20 Critical appraisal of a movie

21 Twenty: prefix

23 Element #27

26 Metal the pipe is made of in the board game Clue

30 "I'll Pin ___ on Your Pillow" (Billy Joe Royal song): 2 wds.

31 Prefix with morph

32 Sophomore plus two years

34 Tiny time unit: abbr., 2 wds.

35 "Ignorance ___ excuse!": 2 wds.

36 Bear witness

38 Nuremberg negative

39 Cold dessert

40 Suffix with cap or coy

41 10th president of the U.S.

Down

1 Constellation between Aquila and Serpens

2 Cellist Pablo

3 Amorphous creatures

4 Public condemnation

5 Véronique, e.g.: abbr.

6 Congo tributary

7 Adjust, in a way

8 Grant

10 Like some stocks, initially

11 With mixed feelings

16 Sugar suffixes

20 Bunk

22 Nile queen, informally

23 Caesars Palace, for example

24 Quick court contest: 2 wds.

25 Sportscaster Bernstein

27 Stamp, as a document

28 Carol opening

29 Practitioner of medicine

33 Cloth for cleaning

37 1968 battle period

147

Across

1 Ms. Helmsley
6 Quintillionth: prefix
10 Get around
11 Suffix with transmission or toxic
13 Certain Middle Eastern entertainer: 2 wds.
15 "Bambi" character
16 Abbr. before a number
17 Airline to The Hague, initially
18 Song that might send you to sleep
20 British verb ending
21 Kung ___ chicken
22 Online publication
24 Rosacea and others
26 Like ___ (probably): 2 wds.
28 Suffix with mod or nod
31 Chain letters?
32 Foxlike
35 Prefix meaning outside
36 Canyon or haban suffix
37 Industrial city in southeastern Serbia
38 Brunch dish: 2 wds.
41 Ionian Island
42 Fluid buildup in the tissues
43 Answer, briefly
44 Dogcatcher's quarry

Down

1 Bar code's place
2 Square: 2 wds.
3 "Va va voom!": 3 wds.
4 Lacking value
5 Innermost sanctuaries in ancient temples
6 Examine methodically
7 One thousand divided by one hundred
8 Eat heartily: 2 wds.
9 Threatening words: 2 wds.
12 ""Him ___ – What's It Gonna Be?" Paul Revere & the Raiders song: 2 wds.
14 Market investment
19 Advance
23 "The game ___!": 2 wds.
25 Paper over: 2 wds.
26 Hold fast
27 Ironic parody
29 Hang around
30 Robert Harris novel
31 Fam. tree member
33 Valuable veins
34 Persuasive article
39 Certain baseball positions, shortly
40 D.C. summer clock setting

148

Across

1 Tops
5 Bed linen items
11 Germany's ___ von Bismarck
12 German W.W. II tank: 2 wds.
13 Russian communications acronym since 1992
14 To the opposite side
15 Startle
17 Come ___ end: 2 wds.
18 Mt. Rushmore's state: 2 wds.
22 Savvy
24 Vittorio De ___
25 Jeremy of basketball fame
26 Get-up-and-go
27 Suit to ___: 2 wds.
29 Chair in Calais
32 Brass instrument sound: hyph.
33 Bricklayers' equipment
34 Club for female students
38 Money, slangily
41 Native Nigerians
42 Sister of Moses
43 Ice sheet
44 Sen. Feinstein
45 Four: prefix

Down

1 ___ de Boulogne (big park in Paris)
2 Ides of March rebuke: 2 wds.
3 Begin again: 2 wds.
4 Listlessness
5 Spots
6 Bar sounds
7 Departure
8 Want ad. initials
9 Change the position of words, letters, etc.: abbr.
10 Bro's partner
16 Dirty dog
19 Like any number by itself
20 Galatea's love in Greek myth
21 Short ridge of material deposited by a melting glacier
22 Cole ___ (KFC side)
23 Canon competitor
28 Introduce gently: 2 wds.
29 Silvery metallic compound
30 "Yoo-___!"
31 Aimless
35 Algerian port
36 Attention-getter
37 River of Belgium
38 Dentist's degree
39 Sundial figure
40 Gp. headed by Heston, initially

149

Across

1 "Analyze This" director
6 Typeface units
11 Praying figure
12 Like a nerd
13 A Gabor sister
14 Circus prop
15 Possession
17 Dental filling
18 Use a needle
21 Made a high ball in golf
23 12 meses
24 Richard ___
25 "The Waste Land" monogram
27 Big maker of A.T.M.s
28 Utah's capital, initially
29 Wreath for the head
31 It can be spent in Naypyidaw
32 Bank holdings: abbr.
33 Traveled by cab: 3 wds.
37 Peter, Paul or Mary
39 Ala. headline city: 1965
40 Some fine porcelain
41 City near Oberhausen
42 It might keep you up at night
43 Nixon commerce secretary Maurice

Down

1 Dallas Cowboy Tony
2 Get ___ deal: 2 wds.
3 Enlarging
4 Move from the margin
5 Hollywood hopeful
6 Excessively self-assertive
7 Former money in Peru
8 Spicy Tex-Mex munchies: 3 wds.
9 Have a bug
10 Jacksonville, for one: abbr.
16 Pathetically inept person: 2 wds.
19 Suffix with insist or infer
20 Contemptible one
21 It makes Sylvester spit
22 Greasy
26 Wraps
30 Swear (to)
32 Great Barrier Island of New Zealand
34 French wave
35 Cyclops, Storm, Wolverine, et al: hyph.
36 McEwan and Somerhalder
37 Medicare minders, initially
38 Killer ___ (excellent computer program)

150

Across

1 Ancient city in upper Mesopotamia
7 Mex. title
11 Distributor of playing cards
12 Academic span
13 Young fish prepared for cooking
14 Slugged, old-style
15 Opposite of pos.
16 Citizen arresters
17 Elevated: 2 wds.
20 Starter: abbr.
21 Bug
25 Part of an office sched.
26 Completely satisfactory: hyph.
27 Top of a clock dial, initially
28 Give out
30 Annual links tournament letters
31 Fidgety
34 Standish of Plymouth Colony
37 No longer edible
38 Many millennia
39 Opposed to war
42 Cosmopolitan competitor
43 Pair of punches in quick succession: hyph.
44 Luxurious resorts
45 Unrequited in love

Down

1 Norton and Wood
2 Merry mo.
3 Money obtained for work
4 Sour fruits
5 Marsh plant
6 ____ Antiqua
7 Computer administrators, briefly
8 Radiation units, initially
9 Mai ____ (cocktails)
10 Johnson of "Love at First Bite"
16 Lousy
17 Terza ____ (Italian verse form)
18 PR people: abbr.
19 Singer Celine and namesakes
22 Process quickly and efficiently
23 Butts: abbr.
24 Familia members
26 Gets on
29 Dunne and Castle
32 Certain steak: hyph.
33 Tennis great Rod ____
34 Artist Nicolaes ____
35 Cry out
36 "Damn Yankees" siren
39 Application form letters
40 Personal ad abbr.
41 Spicy

151

Across

1 Meltdown sites
6 Military aircraft locations, initially
10 Coeur d'____, ID
11 "Casa Dracula" series writer Acosta
13 Opponent of progress or reform
15 "The Fall of the House of Usher" author's monogram
16 TV monitor?
17 Formerly, in Lyon
18 Summer: Fr.
19 Make a new request to be supplied with
21 Makes over
23 It may be heard after a spill
24 Jacket with a mandarin collar
26 Feminine ending
29 Button holder
33 Informal inspection: hyph.
35 Punk offshoot
36 Leb. neighbor
37 Gambling inits.
38 Get-____ (starts)
39 Felines in "Lady and the Tramp": 2 wds.
42 Bye that's bid
43 First name in beauty
44 ____'acte (intermission)
45 They are a sorry lot

Down

1 Calling
2 Soapmaking compound
3 Harvested
4 Env. stuffer
5 Liberate: 2 wds.
6 Exxon alternative
7 Air cooling device
8 "On the Waterfront" star Marlon
9 1979, 1982 and 2011 Oscar winner
12 Australia's ____ Rock
14 Polar features: 2 wds.
20 Debauchee
22 1,024 bytes, briefly: 2 wds.
25 Microbrewery product: 2 wds.
26 Actress Donovan of "Clueless"
27 End of a rugby match: hyph.
28 Good news from a forecaster, often: 2 wds.
30 Emissary
31 Ham
32 Buffets
34 Sister in Strasbourg
40 Came into contact with
41 Coll. whose mascot is Cody Cougar

152

Across

1 Pitcher Martinez
6 Open, in a way
11 One asking impertinent questions
12 Death in Venice
13 Military tactic
14 Pretentious sort
15 Promoter of the "New Look"
17 Baseball's Speaker
18 "Je ne ___ quoi"
20 Other: Sp.
22 Service arm, initially
23 Like some hooks: hyph.
26 Don't come, e.g.
27 Johnson anti-poverty org.
28 Yes, in Yokohama
29 Academic type
31 Do some grilling
32 Tinker with, in a way
33 Ballet burst
34 Columnist Maureen
36 List-ending letters, for short: 2 wds.
38 "A Lesson From ___" (play)
40 O'Connor successor
43 "___ 14 pounds in two weeks!": 2 wds.
44 Skewered Thai dish
45 Saline
46 Tipped rapiers

Down

1 Letter ender, initially
2 "___ tu"
3 Inveterate, unchanging: hyph.
4 Denver university
5 Certain cookie
6 Little League official: abbr.
7 Cosa ___
8 19th-century art movement: hyph.
9 Needle holder
10 H.S. diploma alternatives
16 Optimistic
18 Benchwarmers, for short
19 "Hey, wait ___!": 2 wds.
21 God with a hammer
23 Divas' deliveries
24 To the right, in an atlas
25 Water barrier
30 Most curious
33 Purgative drug
34 Roaster's spot
35 Earthen container
37 Fire a stun gun
39 It's a mess
41 Menlo Park inits.
42 Sounds of woe

153

Across

1 She played Bea in "Kill Bill"
4 Gym round, briefly
7 "The Late Show" network
10 Parked oneself
11 Dot-commer's address, for short
12 Hesitate
13 Colorless gas
15 Needle point?: inits.
16 Durable building material
18 Dick Martin's comic partner Dan
21 Dead, as an engine
22 Concluded
23 Show off, on a Harley, briefly
24 Four in the jaw
29 "Hardly!"
30 Close in on
31 Brain, e.g.
34 Fastens securely
35 Item of cutlery
37 Skirt bottom
38 Bags used when traveling
42 Garden lady
43 Consume
44 Gear tooth
45 Like roses
46 Oinker's pen
47 Deck (out)

Down

1 U.S.S.R. rival, during the Cold War
2 Mother: var.
3 Bill provider, initially
4 Never seem to end: 2 wds.
5 Land of leprechauns
6 Slit in a garment
7 Weak cry of a young bird
8 African language
9 "___ Caroline" (Neil Diamond hit)
14 Egg-shaped wind instruments
17 Devouring voraciously
18 Big bird of stories
19 Genetic lab supplies
20 Cyst
23 Abbr. after some generals' names
25 Surprise and confuse
26 Hallow ending
27 Touch
28 Mins. and mins.
31 Alternative
32 Chaucer pilgrim
33 Played for money
34 Enemy aircraft (military sl.)
36 Dethrone
39 Play the part
40 Gloppy stuff
41 Grade A food

154

Across

1 "___ Like It" (Shakespeare)
6 Soldier of fortune, briefly
10 Has existence
11 City near Buffalo
13 West Yorkshire city
14 Glisten
15 Conscription org.
16 Connect with: 2 wds.
18 Bug-eyed ones, maybe: inits.
19 Some M.I.T. grads
20 Fool
21 Rag
23 Taverns
24 "Hilarious," to texters
25 According to
26 Cries of discovery
28 One of Santa's reindeer
31 Money in Romania
32 "Rescue me!" letters
33 Hotshot
34 Different form of the same thing
36 Light brown
37 Dance partner for Fred
38 Wavelike design
40 Kidney enzyme
41 Make ___ of: 2 wds.
42 Hwys.
43 Bogotá babies

Down

1 Good to go: 2 wds.
2 Spanish snooze
3 Christian Dior rival: 3 wds.
4 Huge Brit. lexicon
5 Pittsburgh giant corp.: 2 wds.
6 Old Testament prophet
7 Relating to grades 1-12: hyph.
8 Second or new birth
9 Synagogue singer
12 Some Chryslers
17 Ending for beef or bump
22 Talking-___ (admonishments)
23 Folds or Stiller
25 "Please Mr. ___" Carpenters hit
26 Architect ___ Aalto
27 Part of an e-mail before the message
28 Mafia boss
29 Game similar to euchre
30 Actresses Godfrey, French and Jones
32 Composer Saint-___
35 French Open winner Nastase
39 Early afternoon

155

Across

1 Card game for two
7 ____-di-dah (pretentious)
10 Angles
11 Hoppy glassful, for short
12 They aren't bound by contracts: 2 wds.
14 Hindu dresses
15 Long period of time
16 Ballistic missile not known for its accuracy
17 "____ Groove" (1985 hip-hop movie)
18 French possessive
19 New delivery
21 Distance races: 2 wds.
22 Lower back pain
25 "Dirty Rotten Cheater" host Dwyer
28 Bubbling
29 Small river fish
30 Having an acid taste
31 Cataract and Grand
33 In close association: hyph.
35 J.F.K. posting: abbr.
36 Ancient Greek headband
37 Welfare org.
38 Marvel Comics supervillain: 2 wds.

Down

1 Wipe out
2 Wispy white cloud
3 Thoreau work, "Faith in ____": 2 wds.
4 Taekwondo great Jhoon ____
5 After-dinner selection
6 Perry Mason creator's initials
7 "____ franca"
8 Most fitting
9 "What dish o' poison ____ dressed him!" ("Twelfth Night"): 2 wds.
13 Brings in
14 J.F.K. sight, initially
17 "The Mikado" role
19 Patricia of "The Subject Was Roses"
20 Coll. major
21 Beach Boys' "Fun, Fun, Fun" car: hyph.
22 Bound
23 Submerged threats of W.W. II: hyph.
24 Piles
25 Eastern prison of old
26 Frozen cause of water blockage: 2 wds.
27 ____ Cayes, Haiti
29 Sink-unclogging brand
31 Watchdog's sound
32 Expressed surprise
34 "Why, ____ be a pleasure!"

156

Across

1 Phrase on some menus: 2 wds.
4 Co. that produced "Rhoda"
7 Journey segment
10 Corporations: abbr.
11 Miler Sebastian
12 "She" in Portuguese
13 Cosmetic applied with a brush
15 "___ for Alibi" (Sue Grafton mystery): 2 wds.
16 Prefix meaning "within"
17 Strong wooden posts
19 Sailor's greetings
21 "I Ain't Never" singer Mel
24 Thompson of "Family"
28 Drop off
29 Mailing list items
30 "Bravo!" shouts
31 Street for kids
32 The Whale constellation
34 Not hide
37 "Showtime!": 2 wds.
41 Patriotic women's org.
42 Violent whirling windstorm
44 Treasure de la Sierra Madre
45 "May ___ of help?": 2 wds.
46 Debussy subject
47 Wander aimlessly
48 Lipton drink
49 Weapon fired from a plane, initially

Down

1 Crowning point
2 It may be floated
3 Kind of D.A.
4 Show biz co.
5 Trunks
6 Substantial
7 Unofficial news source
8 Novelist Wiesel
9 William H., author of "Middle C"
14 Fuse together
18 Hired killer
20 Trendsetting
21 General on some Chinese menus
22 In a bad way
23 Jeans brand
25 Org. with a caduceus logo
26 Rep. rival
27 Enzyme ending
29 Novel in Nuremberg
31 Flashy light
33 "...your cake and ___, too": 2 wds.
34 Lobo song: "Me and You and ___ Named Boo": 2 wds.
35 Legal aide, briefly
36 Prompt
38 Cass Elliot's moniker
39 Music halls
40 Christie novel: 3 wds.
43 Mens ___ (criminal intent)

157

Across

1 Yearly loan figs.
5 Armor breastplates
11 Thailand currency
12 Amateur, for short
13 "___ sow, so shall…": 2 wds.
14 Truth
15 Study of celestial bodies, briefly
16 Dunne and Ryan
17 Perceives sound
19 Japanese robe
21 Some German cars, initially
24 Cecil Campbell, a.k.a. ___ Kamoze
25 Hudson Bay prov.
27 Carbonium, e.g.
28 Historical U.S. non-interventionist group, initially
29 Big name in comics
31 TV, radio, etc.
32 Moon of Neptune
36 Bra size: 2 wds.
39 Start one's PC up again
40 Hawaii County's seat
41 Roman cloak
42 Calif.-Fla. route: 2 wds.
43 Invitation notation
44 Van Morrison's "Brown ___ Girl"

Down

1 Quatrain rhyme scheme, sometimes
2 Bridge option
3 Occurring regularly
4 Dorm room staple
5 Relating to the natural world
6 Ending for theater or church
7 About, on a memo: 2 wds.
8 "Wheel of Fortune" choice
9 Art deco visionary
10 Some milk sources
18 "Is that ___?": 2 wds.
19 Hyundai alternative
20 Like Beethoven's "Pastoral" Symphony: 2 wds.
21 Liveliness, spirit
22 "___ to thee, Moab!" (Num. 21:29)
23 Longtime NBC show
26 Smidge
30 Fonzie's red-haired pal
31 Bucks
32 Ford Explorer Sport ___
33 "Forever Love" singer
34 Natives of Nigeria
35 Fragrant brown balsam
37 Peter Fonda title role, 1997
38 Algae bed?

158

Across

1 Heaps, stacks
6 Like some radios: hyph.
10 Amtrak's bullet train
11 Check recipient
12 Bedouin, e.g.
13 Wit or good looks, e.g.
14 Queen of Thebes in Greek mythology
15 Mem. of the A.B.A.
17 Course list letters
18 Trent Reznor's band, for short
19 2000 Jennifer Lopez movie: 2 wds.
21 Suffix with method or monarch
23 Accustoms
24 Soap starring John Forsythe
26 Show to the door: 2 wds.
28 Massachusetts motto opener
31 Catch
33 Extra pds. of a basketball game
34 Summer hrs. in The Rockies
35 Ping-pong table feature
36 Nov. 11 honoree
37 Composer Albéniz
39 White poplar
41 Faint coloring
42 Cannes award the ___ d'Or
43 JFK takeoff times
44 ___ salts

Down

1 Toasted sandwich
2 Classic, as an image
3 Venture for kids: 2 wds.
4 Italian note
5 Former Egyptian president
6 "___ in alpha": 2 wds.
7 Detective fiction: 2 wds.
8 Lacking strength
9 Aluminum and iron, e.g.
11 Church plates
16 The Globe in London, e.g.
20 Baby-faced
22 City on the Rhone
25 Shade
26 Jew, e.g.
27 Calls things off: 2 wds.
29 Sailor's patron: 2 wds.
30 Honor
32 Military camp (Fr.)
38 Lynch, Holder and Mukasey, initially
40 Protestant denom

59

Across

1 Surround tightly
6 Common pregnancy woe
11 Singer Steve, whose albums include "Terraplane"
12 "A Bar at the Folies-Bergère" painter
13 Preferred route taken by a ship: 2 wds.
15 Sabbath discourses, in short
16 Nels of "Little House on the Prairie"
17 Theatrical awards
19 Treats a violin bow
22 Historic opening?
25 Plane pilot's emergency system: 2 wds.
28 Simile words: 2 wds.
29 Neighboring: 2 wds.
30 Wild ass of Tibet
32 Early in the morning: 2 wds.
35 "Cimarron" author Ferber
39 Compensation for injury or loss
41 One way to fry: 2 wds.
42 Jazz or opera, e.g.
43 "November Criminals" costar Elgort
44 "Wonderwall" band

Down

1 Instrument used to examine the brain, initially
2 Foal's mother
3 ____ Rabbit ("Uncle Remus" character)
4 Stretchy fabric
5 Largest city in Mich.
6 "Wuthering Heights" writer Brontë
7 Beginnings of some pranks
8 Items included in envs.
9 Dramatic opening?
10 Amenhotep IV's god
14 Letter that is not a vowel
18 Minn. neighbor
19 Country-lighting org.
20 Brunch drinks, initially
21 Poseidon's realm
22 For each one
23 Kind of race
24 Eisenhower's command, for short
26 Stimpy's cartoon partner
27 Stimulating drink: 2 wds.
30 Couric of "Today"
31 "____ Survive" Gloria Gaynor hit: 2 wds.
32 Mozart's "Madamina," e.g.
33 Al Gore's state: abbr.
34 Brit. decorations
36 Thunders
37 "Me neither": 2 wds.
38 Donkeys in Dijon
40 "The Inquiry" playwright Betti

160

Across

1 Susan of soaps
6 Hit song from Sarah McLachlan
10 "Get thee gone!"
12 Shake alternative
13 Capital of Poland
14 Radiator sound
15 Go against
17 Void, in Vichy
19 Verizon, for one, initially
20 Lush's sound
23 Faulty Challenger part: hyph.
25 "Gilmore Girls" actress Keiko
27 Church engagement announcement
28 Barrett and Jaffe
29 Amazed: 2 wds.
30 Justin Townes ____, singer whose albums include "Absent Fathers"
31 John ____ Passos, novelist
32 To this day
34 They, in Tours
35 Enumerate
37 Sale caveat: 2 wds.
40 Silver-tongued speaker
43 Legs, slangily
44 Baby Face Nelson's real name, ____ Gillis
45 In such a manner that: 2 wds.
46 Penn and Young

Down

1 Attorney's field
2 Charlottesville sch.
3 North and South states
4 Crescent point
5 Statement of scorn and disbelief: 4 wds.
6 Arthur of tennis fame
7 "Where ____ begin?": 2 wds.
8 They may include photos
9 Battery buys, initially
11 Double dates
16 Car owners' replacements: 2 wds.
17 Bridge call: 2 wds.
18 Heavens: prefix
20 Town in Monroe County, N.Y.
21 Collectively: 2 wds.
22 Situations
24 Compass heading, initially
26 "Don't ____ step farther!": 2 wds.
33 Earth Day subj.
35 Blog feeds, initially
36 Zap with a stunning weapon
37 Grundy and Gilpin, for short
38 ____ Tomé
39 The Monkees' "____ Believer": 2 wds.
41 Vintner's prefix
42 Four Monopoly squares: abbr.

161

Across

1 Brewer Frederick
6 Cut up
11 North of Virginia
12 Spyri heroine
13 Device used to disperse a crowd: 2 wds.
15 1960s campus org.
16 CD-____
17 "Today" rival, briefly
18 Confusions: hyph.
20 Iced tea brand
23 Even, as a score
26 In motion
27 Furniture wood
28 "Went," in Scotland
29 Sign of affection
30 Cry from the saved: 2 wds.
32 Facial offerer
34 City in Valley County, Nebraska
35 File folder feature
38 Detailed description of a person
41 Ontario tribe members
42 Exclamation of frustration: 2 wds.
43 Nicholas Sparks novel: 2 wds.
44 Charges

Down

1 "Hogan's Heroes" for example, initially
2 "Sing me a Song of ____ that is Gone" (R. L. Stevenson poem): 2 wds.
3 Diner orders, initially
4 Prussian pronoun
5 Small dog breed
6 SeaWorld attraction
7 Female lobster
8 Best place to view a boxing match
9 Land in Genesis
10 "True Colors" actress Merrill
14 Hip joint
18 Charley Weaver's hometown: abbr., 2 wds.
19 Wing (prefix)
20 Pill
21 That, in Spanish
22 Sault ____: 2 wds.
24 Federal warning system activated by FEMA
25 Hospital V.I.P.s
27 Relating to the heart
29 Michael of "Superbad"
31 Trigger, for one
32 Roman goddess of hope
33 Go carefully (over)
35 Rolaids rival
36 Like ____ in a trap: 2 wds.
37 Affleck and Stiller
39 Pro ____ (for the time being)
40 Low card

162

Across

1 Life ____ know it: 2 wds.
5 Angry
10 Apocalypse
11 Barrett and Jaffe
12 Some cigarette ends: 2 wds.
14 Assistant for Santa
15 Split
16 Enharmonic of F: 2 wds.
18 Site to prowl for bargains
22 ____ a customer (sale limit): 2 wds.
24 Nigerian tribesman
25 Rakes
27 Biker's invitation to a friend: 2 wds.
29 Former name of the cable network Versus, initially
30 Gravestone, perhaps
32 "____ but known…": 2 wds.
34 Liveliness
37 Four: prefix
39 Green launching pad
40 Covetousness, glutony, etc.: 2 wds.
43 Iran-Contra colonel, informally
44 Other, to Oswaldo
45 "Yum!"
46 Will ____, Grandpa Walton portrayer

Down

1 Pitcher's stat.: 2 wds.
2 Loam and marl, e.g.
3 Borzoi, e.g.
4 One may be seen after a crash, initially
5 Enter forcibly
6 Islamic weight
7 Cutting instrument
8 "The Murders in the Rue Morgue" author's monogram
9 Sheet music markings: abbr.
13 Exit
17 Actress Sue ____ Langdon
19 Involving two separate parties
20 ____ system, initially
21 Hither's opposite
23 "Cabbages and Kings" author: 2 wds.
25 ____ Moo-hyun, 9th president of the Republic of Korea
26 Ending with pay
28 "¡Bravo!"
31 Lipton competitor
33 Slanted type, casually
35 Romance, e.g.
36 "____ no?": 2 wds.
38 Trim to fit, maybe
40 "i" lid
41 Guidonian note
42 Soak, old-style

163

Across

1 Paycheck abbr.
5 Latin I word
9 ___ Lodge (budget motel)
11 Andean animal
12 Insignificant, slangily
13 March follower
14 ___ Leppard (British rockers)
15 Wise guys
17 Some Art Deco works
19 Managua's country, for short
22 Women
24 Gospel singer Winans
25 Sternward
26 "___ unto him who …": 2 wds.
27 Italy's capital, once?
28 "Melt in your mouth" candies: 3 wds.
29 Menu words: 2 wds.
30 Changes course in sailing
31 Bara of the silents
33 Club ___ (vacation resort Co.)
36 "Later, Luis!"
38 Sandcastle setting
40 Perch in a coop
41 Macho guys: hyph.
42 Clothing designer Taylor and TV newswoman Curry
43 Like some profs.

Down

1 Chow
2 Slurpee rival
3 Union of political organizations
4 Part of Q & A, briefly
5 De Siusi or d'Huez, par exemple
6 2011 Seth Green bomb: 3 wds.
7 "What ___ to do?": 2 wds.
8 Chess champion Mikhail
10 Edible mollusk
11 Falls behind
16 Loser to H.C.H.
18 Fighter of pirates, initially
20 SALT concern
21 So-so grades
22 In ___ land (loopy): 2 wds.
23 Yew seed's coat
24 Ice cream treat
26 Ohio tributary
28 Prefix for field or stream
30 Witty remark
32 Eric Cartwright's nickname on "Bonanza"
34 "You are" in Spain
35 Fender-bender result
36 Former Notre Dame coach Parseghian
37 Put on
39 "Hath ___ sister?" (Shakespeare): 2 wds.

164

Across

1 Money in Bangladesh
5 Blues and hip-hop fusion
11 Eisenhower and Turner
12 Flattened at the poles
13 Sights
14 Synapse neighbor
15 First novel in Cather's "Great Plains" trilogy: 2 wds.
17 Former V.P. Agnew
18 Concoct
21 "Eli and the Thirteenth Confession" singer Laura
25 Abbr. on top of some e-mails
26 Bull markets
27 Indian tourist site
29 Giraffe cousins
32 Red Square figure
34 Comrade
38 Computer language iteration: 2 wds.
39 Radiohead's Yorke
41 Brazilian beach resort
42 Bank (on)
43 More crazy
44 Guthrie who sang about Alice

Down

1 Acapulco aunt
2 Sony co-founder Morita
3 "Hold You Tight" singer Tara
4 Birthplace of a saint
5 Former White House nickname
6 "What're ya having?" answer: 2 wds.
7 Attach, in a way: 2 wds.
8 "Chloe ___" (A. A. Milne novel)
9 Oklahoma tribe
10 Fountain or ink

16 Surgical procedures, briefly
18 Alias, in commerce, initially
19 Heartbeat monitor letters
20 TV adjunct
22 "Indeedy"
23 The Engineers of the Liberty League, briefly
24 C.I.A. precursor
28 Oval-shaped nut
29 Even (with): 3 wds.
30 Relations

31 "Peer Gynt" character
33 Greek poem composed of couplets
34 RC, e.g.
35 Fetid, rank
36 NFL star Michael who was the basis for the movie "The Blind Side"
37 Chuck of the N.F.L.
38 ___ Perignon champagne
40 Abyssin character from "Star Wars: Episode IV"

165

Across

1 Smile affectedly or derisively
6 Lawyer's gp.
9 Meeting of spiritualists
10 Lat., Rus., and Ukr., once
11 Calculus for dentists
12 "…will smile and take ___" (Steve Winwood lyric): 2 wds.
13 "Or ___!" (threat ender)
14 Standing
16 John ___, co-creator and star of TBS's "10 Items or Less"
17 Goat-antelope of Sumatra and Kashmir
18 "Spartacus" composer Khachaturian
19 Philosophizing Kierkegaard
20 Slanted type, casually
22 Point on the orbit of a satellite
24 Big brass instrument
28 Needing to shed a few pounds
29 ___ uproar: 2 wds.
30 Spa treatment
32 Head, to Henri
33 Regarding: 2 wds.
34 Morphine, e.g.
36 Wisconsin bodysnatcher Ed
37 Not open
38 Ending for north, south, east or west
39 Sword sharpener

Down

1 Wine bottle's cork, e.g.
2 Mason of "The Goodbye Girl"
3 Temporary suspension of activity
4 Sharp competitor, briefly
5 "From Here to Eternity" actress
6 Guarantee
7 Londoner, e.g.
8 Immaculate: 2 wds.
9 Grave marker
10 Stevie Wonder hit of 1972
15 Foreigners' class, briefly
19 Carrier to Stockholm, for short
21 "___ yellow ribbon …": 2 wds.
22 Humiliator
23 Jelly ingredient
25 Lack of comfort
26 Strike repeatedly with hard blows
27 "On ___ to know basis": 2 wds.
28 Over 21: 2 wds.
31 Ness, e.g.
35 Isr. rival

166

Across

1 Anatomical pouch
4 When doubled, a 1965 Dixie Cups song
7 Lowlife
10 Difficulty
11 Actor Cage, to fans
12 Suffix denoting origin
13 Jamaican friend
14 A, in Mexico
15 Hosp. picture
16 Places for R.N.s
17 Gives a new title to
19 Permanent gov. dept.
21 1998 Sarah McLachlan ballad
22 Clarification lead-in: 2 wds.
23 Lubricant containers
25 Louvre, par exemple
26 ___ double take (looked again): 2 wds.
29 State signing a treaty jointly with others
31 More liquid
32 Never, in German
33 Peer Gynt's mother
34 Man's nickname
35 Pre-album collectibles, for short
36 Markup language descriptor, initially
37 T-shirt sizes: abbr.
38 Univ. in Troy, N.Y.
39 "Star Trek: Voyager" character
40 Cyclops' singleton
41 Damascus is its cap.

Down

1 Indian turnover
2 Beloved
3 Awareness
4 Get accustomed
5 Power a body has when in motion: 2 wds.
6 Source of "The True North strong and free!": 2 wds.
7 Sports regulators
8 "You're in for ___!": 2 wds.
9 Believer
18 Political theorist Hannah
20 Cereal fruit
24 Clearly readable
25 Puddinglike dessert
27 Like some faucets
28 Words to a ship's captain: 2 wds.
29 Fissure
30 Commence

167

Across

1 Kitchen aid
6 "___ Mrs. Smith" (2005 movie): 2 wds.
11 The same, in Strasbourg
12 City in Preble County, Ohio
13 Beetle cars, e.g.
15 Coll. course
16 Start of a Mozart title
17 Most bare
19 City in "The Lost Princess of Oz"
22 Without delay: 3 wds.
24 "And later ___ the crowd thinned out…" (Bob Dylan lyric): 2 wds.
26 "As you ___"
27 Correct: 3 wds.
31 Attorney's income
32 Charge with a lance: 2 wds.
34 "Not again!": 2 wds.
35 One with a six-yr. term
37 Move (text) to another part of a document: 3 wds.
41 ___ ware (Japanese porcelain)
42 "The first time ___ saw your face…": 2 wds.
43 Protestant denom.
44 Kind of rug

Down

1 Guns (an engine)
2 "Shall ___?" ("Do you want me to continue?"): 3 wds.
3 Gauge
4 Canada's ___ Island National Park
5 Look for again
6 "It ___ lot to me": 2 wds.
7 Foam at the mouth
8 Grazed
9 Nanette's negative
10 Internet protocol inits.
14 Become aware, with "up"
18 Gossip, slangily
19 Hoi polloi: 2 wds.
20 TV adjustment: abbr.
21 Manhattan addition
23 Belt
24 "Pow!" response
25 Navigator's dir.
28 Kind of cuisine
29 Fasten
30 Runs off to get married
33 Colorful aquarium dweller
34 Boat propellers
36 Pooch in TV's "Topper"
37 Inc., in Paris
38 Man in blue: abbr.
39 Randy's rink partner
40 Bird: prefix

168

Across

1 Silent Marx brother
6 Respectful title for a woman
11 On ___ (rebellious): 2 wds.
12 Turner's 1986 rock autobiography: 2 wds.
13 Ted ___, Chevy Chase's role on "Chuck"
14 Fender guitar model, briefly
15 Booker White's style of music: 2 wds.
17 Thickheaded
18 Middle-___ (fiftysomething)
20 Part of a tea set
25 Buck who won a Nobel Prize
27 Very minor movie stars: hyph.
28 Not alert
30 Blows up, initially
31 Accepted
33 In right now: 3 wds.
38 Developed
39 Actress Anouk
40 Screen with blips
41 Herman's Hermits lead
42 Gives off
43 White-tailed birds

Down

1 Difficult
2 First part of an encyclopedia, maybe: 3 wds.
3 "The ___" (Evander Holyfield's nickname): 2 wds.
4 Theater area
5 Sitcom's Mork or Orson, e.g.
6 Inform wrongly
7 Outermost Aleutian island
8 Desperately urgent
9 Collections of anecdotes
10 Place-setting base
16 Univ. degrees
18 Psychiatrists' org.
19 Some stoves, initially
21 Lying beneath what is revealed
22 Aromatic bark used as a spice
23 More or less: abbr.
24 Some N.F.L.ers
26 Written communications
29 Oom-___
32 "The Family Circus" cartoonist Bil
33 "Sabre Dance" composer Khachaturian
34 City located in San Joaquin County, California
35 Exam for would-be attys.
36 Cell component
37 Wide widths, initially
38 "Who ___ you?"

169

Across

1 Out of touch, with "out"
7 Brief and to the point
9 Daughter of Theia
12 Hazy
13 Route letters
14 Native of Benin, Nigeria
15 Of greater than average duration
17 Curses
20 Kapok-producing tree
21 Barcelona's country
23 Civil rights org. once led by Stokely Carmichael
24 Crescent-shaped symbol
26 Elevator man
28 High moorlands, to Brits
30 Catches on, with "up"
32 Roost
34 Absorb oxygen
36 Part of a nest egg, for short
37 Born as, in the society pages
38 Advent
41 "Heavens!"
42 General rule regarding moral conduct
43 Cubic meters

Down

1 Changed direction abruptly
2 Animals that eat bamboo
3 Done
4 Rank above maj.
5 Suffix with butyl
6 Face with digits
8 "Peter Pan" critter
9 Brit. operator of a railroad locomotive: 2 wds.
10 Year before the A.D. system began: 2 wds.
11 Ridge of ice on a glacier
16 Be cozy, in a way
18 1938 French novel also translated as "The Diary of Antoine Roquentin"
19 Absolution cause
22 ____ Haven, CT
25 Spinning fun
26 Because of, with "to"
27 Ringworm
29 Predicament
31 Prelude to a duel
33 Brings to an end
35 Blows it
39 The "R" in AARP
40 Curling surface

170

Across

1 Writer Sholem ____
5 Popular record label, once
11 Mutual fund fee
12 Cuts the fleece from a sheep
13 Boone's nickname
14 Rachmaninov or Prokofiev
15 Bee: prefix
16 Las Vegas stake
17 Night time, to Burns
18 ____ Bluff National Monument
21 Playwright Chekhov and actor Yelchin
23 English 101 verb: 2 wds.
27 John of farming equipment
28 Submarine detector
29 Gunfighter at the O.K. Corral
30 Trite or obvious remark
31 In short supply
33 Having no value
36 Periods after a tie, in sports: abbr.
37 Jerry Lewis's telethon org.
40 Ursus ____ (brown bear)
42 Five-time Wimbledon champ
43 Puzzle based on Latin Squares
44 Locale of Tolkien's "The Prancing Pony"
45 Shoe part
46 Six, in San Jose

Down

1 "Crimes and Misdemeanors" actor
2 Ivory, e.g.
3 Metallic cylinder used for storage
4 Cholesterol carrier, initially
5 Holdings
6 "Gone With the Wind" name
7 Suffix with hotel
8 Guru
9 Bird's home
10 X ____ "x-ray": 2 wds.
16 Matter of contention
19 Marine ____
20 Unemotional person
21 Ending for orange or Gator
22 Teacher's union letters
24 Again: 2 wds.
25 "Faugh!"
26 Prior, to poets
28 Certain cameras: inits.
30 What you might put on a dog
32 "Chain Gang" singer Sam
33 President, in modern Hebrew
34 "Who Can ____ To" (2014 musical movie): 2 wds.
35 Calculator displays
38 Eins, zwei, ____
39 Historical periods
41 Little one
42 Air-gun load

171

Across

1 Basketball net holder
4 Crook's alter ego, for short
7 Seventh enlisted army rank, initially
10 Disdained
12 Completely
13 Word with the same meaning as another
14 Its U stands for "under"
15 Grammarian's "Who's there?" reply: 3 wds.
16 Doctors' assn.
17 Certain navel, slangily
19 Signs on for another term: hyph.
21 Broadway hit sign, initially
22 "High Anxiety" director Brooks
23 In perpetuity
29 "___ geht's?" (German "How are you?")
30 Hoops player's org.
31 Gangs of people who work on ships
34 Marketing strategy: hyph.
36 Musical notes
37 ___ Magalhães, Brazilian national baseball player
39 Script righters: abbr.
40 Opens, as a door
43 Thou, to a frau
44 Specialty dairy brand
45 410, to Caesar
46 Pompous sort
47 Decorates with bathroom tissue, for short

Down

1 System for distributing news to Web users, initially
2 More than cool
3 Supervise
4 Singer Lennox
5 Piano parts
6 Fan, supporter
7 Hindu holy man
8 Plop down
9 Ad biz awards
11 Flat round bread cooked on a griddle
17 Org. founded by George Soros in 1993, initially
18 Prefix for dynamic
20 Colonnade tree
22 Chinese noodles dish
24 "Gross!"
25 River through Cracow
26 Form of baseball: 3 wds.
27 Baseball statistic that's higher for heavy hitters, initially
28 Suffix with Salvador
31 Dimin.'s musical opposite
32 Made over
33 Antique auto
34 Soothing sprinklings
35 "Ain't No Woman Like the One ___": 2 wds.
38 Poet Coolbrith et al.
41 "Napoleon Dynamite" role
42 1960s protest grp.

172

Across

1 Lion-headed Egyptian goddess
5 The house in Don Quixote: 2 wds.
11 Nick and Nora's dog
12 Chemical cousin
13 Linebacker Junior
14 Father Christmas, familiarly: 2 wds.
15 "Am ___ risk?": 2 wds.
16 Drilling org.
17 Former Toronto pitching ace
19 Caught, in a way
23 Kitchen gadget company
24 Nine, in Spanish
25 Empty talk
27 Motorist's choices: abbr.
28 Funny Mike
30 Puerto Rico clock setting, initially
31 Rid of vermin
32 Dam on the Coosa River
35 Las ___ (12:00, in Spain)
37 Financial regulators, initially
38 Green film on copper
41 Kitty
42 Delights
43 Thun's river
44 Break away
45 Holy Fr. women

Down

1 Footing
2 Have ___ (park it): 2 wds.
3 Seller of pens, paper, etc.
4 Cross design
5 Speech problem
6 Back
7 Large open area inside a building
8 French friend
9 Not sweet
10 Ship for pairs
16 Letters indicating price flexibility
18 Hand over to the authorities of another country
20 Woman's undergarment
21 Garden of Eden woman
22 "Der Ring ___ Nibelungen"
25 Mil. officer's charge
26 Yes, to a sailor
29 Threw rocks at
30 Leave astonished
33 Mall component
34 Corporate department
36 Situation
38 Anatomical foot
39 Heavy beer
40 Middle X or O
41 Faux-___

173

Across

1 Antioxidant-rich berry
5 Sydney ___ House
10 Without: Fr.
11 Associated with flowers
12 Literary collections
13 Utterly senseless
14 Classic exercises: hyph.
16 Scolder's sounds
17 Sound of laughter 2 wds.
19 Ethnic group of Vietnam
21 Most close
25 Group of whales
26 Newspaper that once owned About.com: inits.
27 "___ Am Mariah" (Mariah Carey album): 2 wds.
28 Small beards
30 Prefix with propyl
31 Improvises: hyph.
33 Bandy words
36 "Precious Moments" giftware company
39 Swine enclosure
41 Told a whopper
42 Surfaces for walking
43 Noble title
44 Plant with laxative properties
45 Chemical endings

Down

1 Hutchinson and Candler
2 Ability question: 2 wds.
3 Detested thing or person
4 Topic under discussion
5 Former name of the cable network Versus, initially
6 Campaign need
7 Geologists' studies
8 File's partner
9 Pub quaffs
11 Camera device: 2 wds.
15 Was the author of
18 Has a traditional meal: 2 wds.
19 Breakfast food
20 1957 Physics Nobelist Tsung-___ Lee
22 Discharge
23 French pronoun
24 Pedro's uncle
29 Sport fisher's catch
32 "My Life on Trial" author Melvin
33 Coppertone nos.
34 Huge heap
35 Stravinsky ballet
37 Wrap in waxed cloth
38 Long ones are hard to beat
40 Historian's time

174

Across

1 Bake in individual dishes, as eggs
6 Plagued, as by problems
11 ___ K., "Life in the Foodchain" singer
12 Ski resort in Ludlow, VT
13 Rickman and Hale
14 "At the Center of the Storm" author George
15 China neighbour, for short
16 "Xanadu" rock group, initially
18 Savings plan, briefly
19 Sixth sense, briefly
20 Exchange punches in the ring
21 Wildcat's strike
22 Enlist again: hyph.
24 Fashion illustrator of the 1920s
25 Horse, in poetry
27 Feel angry: 2 wds.
28 Actor Gregory
29 Dynamic introduction?
30 Prefix with directional
31 Bond initial rating from Moody's
32 Feb., Mar., Apr., etc.
35 J.F.K. search party?
36 Put money on the line
37 It's five hrs. behind UTC
38 Part of the leg
40 Health, in Le Havre
42 ___ Island National Monument
43 Prefix with national or net
44 "Touched by an Angel" co-star
45 "Sounder" actress Cicely

Down

1 Ezekiel ___, arch-enemy of Iron Man
2 Apertures
3 Too small to make a significant difference
4 ___ Tin Tin
5 Plot device in "Citizen Kane"
6 Product that prevents wrinkles
7 Squeeze (out a living)
8 Temporary mental lapses: 2 wds.
9 Title for a retired professor, maybe
10 Smashed beyond repair, slangily
17 Take a bough
23 It's a scream
24 Sonnet ending
25 Make an explosive or spitting sound
26 Kind of strength
27 Scrams: 2 wds.
29 Dental org.
31 Demean
33 Prefix with arthritis
34 Back of a boat
39 "___ for insect": 2 wds.
41 Some quantity

175

Across

1 Blind strip
5 Drink of the Hindu gods
11 Holy man
12 Protect, as freshness: 2 wds.
13 Fashion model Wek
14 Called
15 Small, slender long-tailed parrot
17 They may be paid with interest
21 Maxima maker
25 Big bore
26 Largish combo
27 Eucalyptus eater
28 Dinner, lunch or brunch
29 Had a longing
30 Buckle up: 2 wds.
32 Doesn't dwell on: 2 wds.
37 Thistlelike plant
40 "___ Baby" ("Hair" song)
41 Prompt
42 Depletes
43 Impose a fine
44 Be bratty

Down

1 Smack
2 Fa followers: hyph.
3 Part of A.A.R.P.: abbr.
4 Bangladesh currency unit
5 Back at sea
6 Getty Center architect Richard
7 Was a fink to: 2 wds.
8 "___ say!"
9 Decorative noose
10 Common connector
16 "Still Pitching" author Jim
18 Irish isle
19 Agitate
20 W.W. I biplane
21 ___ de plume (literary aliases)
22 "Law and Order" actor-rapper: hyph.
23 Asterisk
24 Rastafarian's messiah
27 Jennings, Caminiti and Burns
29 Gives way
31 Pounding parts
33 Bridge call
34 Org. for dealers in rare books
35 Nurses, in a bar
36 "Working Girl" girl
37 "La-la" lead-in
38 Suffix with adopt or address
39 Mornings, for short

176

Across

1 They often include a photo
4 ABC morning show, for short
7 "___ Turn" (traffic sign): 2 wds.
8 Wrath or envy, e.g.
9 Doggie's doc
12 Very close in resemblance
15 Had been
16 Romantic novelist Glyn
17 Protective fold of skin
19 Cookbook verb
20 Biblical kingdom
21 Post-Christmas event
22 Itty-bitty
24 Houston Dynamo's org.
26 Pick up
27 Goya's "Duchess of ___"
29 Peut-___ (maybe, in Marseilles)
31 Exude
32 Elapse: 2 wds.
35 Dispatch boats
37 Common small crake
38 Prayer at the end of a church service
40 Having one sharp (music): 2 wds.
41 Disney deer
42 ___-smoking section
43 P.D. rank
44 "That's more than I needed to hear!", initially

Down

1 Wide-eyed: 2 wds.
2 One of the Seven Dwarfs
3 God: 2 wds.
4 Aide in the Army, initially
5 Thing that has both advantages and disadvantages: 2 wds.
6 Indigo plant
9 Favorable or commanding position: 2 wds.
10 Star, in Paris
11 Harness ring
13 Move, realtor-style
14 Beauty pageant title
18 "___ the Walrus": 2 wds.
22 Spicy condiment
23 A natural in craps
25 N.L. Central team inits.
28 Basilica section
30 "The Brady Bunch" actor Robbie
33 Quidditch player's need
34 One-named New Age musician born in Greece
36 Keats creations
39 Alley animal

Across

1 Body underwriting private bank accounts, initially
5 H–M connection
9 Military academy freshman
10 Strange, odd
12 Middle Eastern porter
13 ___ pad (kind of tablet)
14 Gilled mushroom
16 Detect
17 Junior
18 Small batteries' letters
20 Box office sign, initially
21 Extremities
23 Measurement for the fineness of silk
25 If nothing else: 2 wds.
27 Sleeveless leather jacket of old
29 Soccer org. founded in 1904
32 Kind of poem
33 Digital readout, for short
35 "Delta of Venus" writer
36 New Zealander, informally
38 "When the Snow is on the Roses" singer: 2 wds.
40 Les ___-Unis
42 Leave one's bed
43 Animals' backs
44 1983 Streisand film
45 Nutritional info. letters
46 Carbonated soft drink

Down

1 Large cider bottle
2 Ask for money for helping solve a crime: 3 wds.
3 Construction beam: hyph.
4 "Brief Encounter" actress Johnson
5 Brainpower stats., initially
6 Extends out or over
7 Holds that thought: 4 wds.
8 1831 Poe poem originally entitled "A Paean"
9 Part of a developmental sequence
11 Moving part of an engine
15 Fall in pitch of the voice
19 Halibut habitat
22 NASDAQ buy
24 Bouncing letters
26 "___ Darlin'" (1959 song)
27 Talked humorously
28 Newspaper employee
30 Annual San Antonio event
31 "The Fault in Our Stars" costar Elgort
34 Critical times: hyph.
37 "___ Gift" (W. C. Fields movie): 2 wds.
39 Of Mars (comb. form)
41 Finnair rival

178

Across

1 Chevy ____ (comic actor)
6 Cousin of a raccoon
11 Shack
12 Sen. Hatch
13 Humdingers
14 Sovereignty
15 Become like the people of the USA in customs
17 What a plant often grows from: 2 wds.
18 Washington hockey team, casually
21 The yellow Teletubby: hyph.
25 U.S.A.F. weapon
26 Notable time period
27 Snap or staple
31 Bat Masterson's weapon
32 Five Norse kings
34 Gymnastic moves
39 "Super Breakout" company
40 Put into cardboard containers: 2 wds.
41 British friends
42 IRA-establishing legislation
43 Win by ____: 2 wds.
44 Enjoys, as benefits

Down

1 Vittles
2 Refine, as a skill
3 Birds as a class of vertebrates
4 "Perfect sleeper" mattresses
5 Someone ____ (not mine)
6 Pupil's cover
7 Frozen french fries brand: hyph.
8 Mex. neighbor
9 Andrews of "The Mod Squad"
10 Roadside stopover
16 Catholicism or Hinduism: abbr.
18 Half-____ (latte order): abbr.
19 Little battery letters
20 Theresa May and Tony Blair, for two: abbr.
22 Open-air gambling milieu
23 Son of Prince Valiant
24 Professional teacher org.
28 Spanish constructions
29 Nancy Drew's aunt
30 Get the drop on
31 Where some errands are run, shortly: hyph.
33 "Animal House" college
34 ____ impasse (unable to go further): 2 wds.
35 "Lydia" poet
36 Ornamental plant
37 Astrological border
38 Marienbad et al.
39 Health org.

79

Across

1 Sledder's spot
5 It parallels the radius
9 Craze
10 Extremely: 2 wds.
12 Play the role of: 2 wds.
13 De ___ (in effect)
14 Musician and record producer, ___ Turner
15 Excessive amount
17 Dungeons & Dragons game co., initially
18 Bilbao bear
19 Chicago to Nashville dir.
20 Switzerland's longest river
22 Handel opera, "___ and Galatea"
24 "No way!": 2 wds.
26 S. African livestock pen
29 "Breathless" star Richard
31 Late humor writer Bombeck
32 River in northeastern Portugal
34 Trading abbr.
36 Designer monogram under the Gucci label
37 Confidentially: 2 wds.
39 Inflight est.
40 Toyota marque 2003–16
41 "Daphnis and Chloë" composer
43 Disorder
44 "The Moor's Account" author Lalami
45 Townshend of "The Who"
46 Actors Mineo and Viscuso

Down

1 Tool for cutting metal
2 Given to asking questions
3 "Baby Be-Bop" author Francesca ___ Block
4 Dogie catcher
5 Depose from priesthood
6 Baguette or challah, e.g.
7 Undesirable thing that must be accepted: 2 wds.
8 Nay sayers
9 Rum cocktail: 2 wds.
11 Fawn over, with "on"
16 The Beach Boys' "Surfin' ___"
21 Toronto to Ottawa dir.
23 More than annoyance
25 Beat severely
27 Beers from the Netherlands
28 Random chorus syllables: 3 wds.
30 U.F.O. crew members
32 Mrs. Addams, to Gomez
33 Open, as a toothpaste tube
35 "Save" shortcut on some computers: abbr., 2 wds.
38 Underground part of a plant
42 Motorist's org.

180

Across

1 Language of Israel
7 Neighbor of Minn.: 2 wds.
11 Brooks Robinson, e.g.
12 Manicurist's tool
13 Took back
15 City on the Moselle
16 ___ Tafari (Haile Selassie)
17 Eating place
21 W.W. I army, initially
22 Extended
25 Nepal or Japan, e.g.: hyph.
28 Is suspicious
29 Zodiac animal
30 Causally connected: 2 wds.
33 Sack
35 DineEquity restaurant chain
36 Those who've just had their first birthday: hyph.
41 ___ in a blue moon
42 Industrial city on Lake Michigan
43 "The Odd Couple" director
44 Waste container

Down

1 Old TV knob, briefly
2 Afore
3 Marcel Marceau persona
4 Campus quarters
5 "Somebody ___ Guy" (Jocelyn Brown single)
6 African area under Moroccan control: 2 wds.
7 Unavailable to purchase in a gallery, initially
8 Take no notice of
9 Caesar: "___ iacta est" ("The die is cast")
10 Reebok competitor
14 Pound and Klein
17 Embargoes
18 Pack of paper
19 Ship area behind the bridge house
20 Bankbook abbr.
23 South Dakota, to Pierre
24 Expo presentation
26 Grosse ___, Mich.
27 Lt. Col. North, to friends
31 Hartebeests
32 Geologic period
33 Audience sounds
34 Sicilian city
37 "Undoubtedly"
38 Suffix for carbo or catho
39 Kind of test letters
40 One in 100: abbr.

181

Across

1 Ticket, in slang
6 "Butterfield 8" author
11 Actress Kate of "Dynasty"
12 Kind of panel
13 Leslie of "An American in Paris"
14 Ado: hyph.
15 "The lady ___ protest too much"
17 Lascivious longing
18 Torque-transmitting tooth
20 Prefix with distant
22 Simple quatrain pattern
24 With wisdom
28 Lacking backbone
30 Rapid series of short loud sounds
31 Grow irate: 2 wds.
33 Hawaiian goose
34 Bug repellent brand
36 Kia or Miata
37 Nile slitherers
40 Proposal opposed by Perot: abbr.
42 Dove, at times
44 Earthquake
47 Pepsi-Cola inventor Bradham
48 Band
49 RR postings
50 City and county in Texas

Down

1 Med. school grad.
2 Emma in "The Avengers" (1998)
3 Rummy or whist: 2 wds.
4 Suffix with buck or kang
5 Aunt in Avignon
6 City in western Kyrgyzstan
7 Violent young troublemaker
8 Matty or Felipe of baseball
9 Stadium sounds
10 Smell ___ (be suspicious): 2 wds.
16 Mil. command centers
18 Andrew Lloyd Webber musical
19 2016 award for Jayne Houdyshell
21 Pol. union of 1958
23 Food for avians
25 Voting event
26 River through Yakutsk
27 1914 battle line
29 Irish Sea feeder
32 B.S., e.g.
35 Kind of bud
37 Bkprs.' records
38 Overcharge, slangily
39 North ___ or South ___
41 Graceful bird
43 Some Heisman Trophy winners, initially
45 "___ hear!": 2 wds.
46 Brit. legislators

182

Across

1 Commonly
4 Mason's tool
10 Financial columnist Marshall
12 Aim
13 Author ___ Stanley Gardner
14 Tangled
15 Brosnan TV role
17 Courtney's role on "Friends"
19 Music with jazzlike riffs
22 Pain reducing brand
23 Three-letter metal
24 Early touring car
25 Antelope with cowlike horns
26 ___ roll (winning): 2 wds.
27 Big World Cup power: abbr.
28 Donny, Marie, Jimmy, et al.
30 Humanities dept.
31 Insect-trapping plant
32 "___ Honor" (2008 romcom): 2 wds.
34 Elk
39 Sonoran Indian
40 Unit of linked genes
41 "Et voilà!": hyph.
42 State in western Malaysia
43 Sunshine on the clock, initially

Down

1 A matador hears them
2 Resort in southwestern Florida: 2 wds.
3 Christian doctrine of design and purpose
4 Taking a long while to do: hyph.
5 Genetic info. carrier
6 Giant slugger Mel
7 Dripping
8 Chemical ending
9 Ford Galaxie 500 letters
11 Blass competitor
16 Foreign languages
18 Female college graduate
19 Totally lifeless: 2 wds.
20 "The Last ___" (DevilDriver album): 2 wds.
21 Literary olios
22 Keep from escaping
29 Pindar, for one
33 Formal authorization
34 Doo-___ (1950s music style)
35 Baboon's cousin
36 Female swan
37 George Gershwin's brother
38 Bricks unit?

83

Across

1 Fort Collins campus, initially
4 Game with "It"
7 Religious day: abbr.
10 Canadian TV channel, initially
11 Blood-group letters
12 Paddle lookalike
13 Atmospheric condition that brings rain: hyph.
16 Precious people
17 Lost color
18 Kind of deer
19 Failing grades
20 Parisian playgrounds
22 Bloodsucker
25 From a distance
26 Like lemons
27 Cone bearers
29 Melodic
30 Island where Brando lived: abbr.
31 Bus. ltr. abbr.
32 Shade of gray
34 Conductor Zubin
37 No clue
39 Every little bit
40 Mighty long stretch
41 Writer Anais
42 Triangle of railway track used for turning
43 Double twist
44 Defunct telecom giant letters

Down

1 Icy
2 Dark purple fruit
3 Indefensible
4 Former ABC TV president Jamie
5 Beame or Fortas
6 "Good news" preached by Jesus
7 Critical examination of one's motives: hyph.
8 Rhine feeder
9 Engendered
14 Produce young
15 Acrobat's need, at times: 2 wds.
20 Father, to Huck Finn
21 Movie-cataloguing grp.
23 ___ de coeur
24 Cellphone co.
28 Actress North
29 Grand Prix site: 2 wds.
32 "Heartbreak House" writer
33 Comic Tomlin
35 French roof
36 "The Diary of ___ Frank"
38 Opposite of yeses

184

Across

1 Strain
6 Dustin Hoffman role of 1969
11 Word after time or money
12 Hatred
13 Coins often given away: 2 wds.
15 First name in tyranny
16 Faucet brand
17 Jollity
20 4.0 is a perfect one, initially
22 Islet
23 Trusted male friend, slangily: 2 wds.
27 Weekends are full of it: 2 wds.
29 Cryptographer
30 Big Apple educ. institution
31 Ending for real or surreal
32 Part of Y.W.C.A.
33 Easy as falling off ___: 2 wds.
36 Inst. in Nashville
38 Extremely courageous
43 How cardinals are garbed: 2 wds.
44 Homer hero of 1961
45 Starts a pot
46 Pen name of Theodor Geisel, Dr. ___

Down

1 Some coll. degrees
2 Grammy category
3 Mrs. Juan Peron
4 Goosebump-raising
5 1856 Stowe novel
6 "Ruh-___!" (Scooby-Doo phrase)
7 Inflexible
8 Baseball's Martinez
9 Black Kapital Records founder Knight
10 Foreboding phenomenon
14 Tube of finely ground tobacco wrapped in paper
17 Kind of force
18 Claim on a property
19 Suffix with path or synth
21 Fishing locale
23 Flood residues
24 Hr. divs.
25 Grammy winners Winehouse and Grant
26 Nine in Nuremberg
28 Dressed very elegantly
32 Psychic glows
33 Saturn's end?
34 Actor Mark ___-Baker
35 Dutch astronomer who proved the galaxy rotates
37 Snead and Shepard
39 Horse height measurements: abbr.
40 Broadway bio starring Robert Morse
41 Dortmund dessert
42 Grad. degree

185

Across

1 Scottish TV pioneer
6 Little rascal
11 Let out, possibly
12 Absalom's sister
13 Take apart
15 Place for roasting
16 ___-Bo
17 1995 triple Grammy winner
19 Third-century date
22 Con tricks: hyph.
25 Not all that close
26 Floor of a fireplace
28 Barack Obama's Secretary of Education ___ Duncan
29 Humiliated
30 1950 film noir classic
31 Make a trade
32 Govt. watchdog
33 Sleazy newspapers
37 Book in which marriages and births are recorded: 2 wds.
41 Dinar spender
42 Arctic or Atlantic
43 Monster
44 Necessities

Down

1 1990s pop group Color Me ___
2 Other things: Lat.
3 "Me here!," more grammatically: 2 wds.
4 Comfort
5 Rx givers: abbr.
6 Pilfer
7 Proceeded
8 Embassy head: abbr.
9 Bad: Fr.
10 Opposite of post-
14 Store secretly: 2 wds.
18 Skillful, facetiously
19 Corp. money managers
20 Walking aid
21 Incensed
22 Roe source
23 Architect Saarinen who designed the St. Louis Gateway Arch
24 Blue Nile source lake
25 Not for free: 3 wds.
27 Govt. agency once headed by Hector Barreto
31 Divvy up
32 One in Oberammergau
34 As busy as ___: 2 wds.
35 Happy
36 D.C. group
37 Little lie
38 "Who ___ we kidding?"
39 Kid's cry
40 "___ appetit!"

186

Across

1 Exam for future MDs
5 City on the Rio Grande
11 Christmas
12 Singer Cara and others
13 There are five in "The Twelve Days of Christmas": 2 wds.
15 Grandma: Ger.
16 Spot in the countryside
17 Tulsa sch. named for a televangelist
18 "Catch the Wind" singer
20 Ms. Benaderet
21 Slick material
22 Red or Brave, for short
23 Rising times
26 Odes, sonnets, etc.
27 Dwarf buffalo
28 Cut with the teeth
29 Hoover ____
30 Most fashionable or stylish, slangily
34 Author LeShan
35 From ____ Z: 2 wds.
36 Eastern life principle
37 Feeling of terror and anxiety: 2 wds.
40 Come to light
41 Breezy
42 Land
43 Laine of jazz

Down

1 Expression of awe: 2 wds.
2 Former governor of New York State, Mario ____
3 Edgar ____ Poe
4 Kennedy or Turner
5 In direct descent
6 Firth of Clyde island
7 Outdoor sports store
8 Confer honor upon
9 College conferrals
10 Burial receptacle
14 Mr. Presley
19 Mrs. Chaplin
22 Succinct denial: 2 wds.
23 Did great, golf-wise: 2 wds.
24 Having been challenged: 3 wds.
25 European country
26 Burgundy grape
28 Scientific study of plants
30 Be silent, in music
31 Market online: hyph.
32 Start of a French oath
33 Capital of Japan
38 Archipelago unit: abbr.
39 Part of X-X-X

187

Across

1 Roof-supporting beam
7 "Who ___?" (slangy query)
10 Light reflected by a planet
11 Type size
12 Spooky sort
13 Not imagined
14 Product such as lipstick, etc.
16 Give the eye
19 Little piggy
20 Intimidate
22 Extreme curve in a river
26 "Likewise"
27 Encircle as a military tactic
28 Difficult to scale
29 Oil of wintergreen, e.g.
30 Masefield play "The Tragedy of ___"
32 Quaker's "you"
33 Periodic paperback publication
37 Exploitative one
38 Elvis Presley's "Love Me ___"
42 Pint-sized
43 Elongated cluster of flowers
44 Work on a doily
45 Make accessible: 2 wds.

Down

1 Served like sushi
2 Inn serving
3 "Arlington Road" org.
4 Celebration of a 300th anniversary
5 Taro corm or plant
6 Fowl place
7 Losing proposition?
8 Health food berry
9 Soft mineral
11 Antecedence
15 Large herbivore
16 Phil Collins: "Against All ___"
17 Stride or canter
18 Fretted instrument
21 November birthstone
23 One of Alcott's "little women"
24 It consists of a concave and a convex segment
25 "The Way We ___"
31 Funny Car fuel
33 Stray dog, often
34 Home of most Indians
35 Lady's counterpart
36 Certain tide
39 Lion's home
40 Flightless Australian
41 Congressperson: abbr.

188

Across

1 "Steady as ___ goes"
4 Bit
7 Prefix with cycle
10 Vintner's prefix
11 Genre of music heard in "Garden State"
12 Dark time for poets
13 Brick structures with a space between them: 2 wds.
16 "Carry ___" Joan Baez song: 2 wds.
17 ___ M. M. Blume, "Everybody Behaves Badly" author
18 Buckeye State sch.: 2 wds.
20 City of central China
21 Org. for part-time soldiers
24 D.C. advisory group
25 "The ___ Family" sitcom series starring Shirley Jones
28 End of some scores
29 Pituitary hormone, initially
30 Queen Anne's ___ (flower)
32 Popular exercise technique: 2 wds.
36 Right away: 2 wds.
39 Overripe fruit problem
40 Utica flower?: 2 wds.
42 Hugs, symbolically
43 President pro ___
44 Prefix with management
45 NBC sketch series
46 Radical grp. of the 1960s
47 "Quiet down!" sounds

Down

1 Prefix with linguistics
2 Candy bar option
3 Summary stanza
4 Sleuth: abbr.
5 ___ nitrate
6 Boxer Riddick
7 Informing by words
8 Let go
9 Harmonious: 2 wds.
14 "The Fault ___ Stars" (John Green novel): 2 wds.
15 Dolt
19 Court grp.
22 Curve
23 "Cross Creek" director Martin
25 1986 movie costarring Tom Berenger
26 Inebriating drink
27 Abu ___
28 Cottonwoods
31 Old Spanish queen
33 Little people
34 Forest tree
35 Others, in Mexico
37 100 lb. units
38 Managed, with "out"
41 Real estate ad abbr.

189

Across

1 Small container with divisions
6 Hearing-related
11 "The Barber of Seville," e.g.
12 "I'm Putting All My Eggs ___ Basket" (song)
13 Lamebrain
14 1701 in Roman numerals
15 Wordsworth's forte: 2 wds.
17 Single facet: 2 wds.
18 Food from a hen
19 TV collie
23 Province of eastern Belgium
26 Hebrew letter: var.
27 "___ hatter" (insane): 3 wds.
29 Vehicle for a large family
30 Obsessive fan
33 Dreamy, indolent sort: hyph.
36 "It ain't over till it's over" speaker
37 One of the official languages of India
38 Broadcasting: 2 wds.
39 "Parenthood" actress Sarah
40 Drew in mysteries
41 Enjoyed immensely: 2 wds.

Down

1 Hair-grooming tool
2 Written defense of one's beliefs
3 Insane
4 Pilotless plane
5 N.Y. squad, familiarly
6 Tried to hit: 2 wds.
7 Take off clothes
8 Fabled fliers
9 Ending to appear or avoid
10 Island ring?
16 Cruella de ___, 101 Dalmatians antagonist
18 Shade tree
20 Cut corners: 2 wds.
21 "Go on, take a risk!": 3 wds.
22 Night of poetry
24 Relating to the stomach
25 Tidal mouth of a river
28 "___ in apple": 2 wds.
31 Feminist author Tanenbaum
32 Fort Knox measurement
33 She played Glinda in "The Wiz"
34 "The Plague" city
35 File
36 "___ chance!"

190

Across

1 Marshes
5 Pedicurist's stone
11 Like endangered species
12 Hank who voices Chief Wiggum
13 Residents: suffix
14 Lemonlike fruit
15 Reprimand severely
17 Suffix with saliva or scintilla
18 Himalayan creature
22 With reference to
25 Homer's TV neighbor
26 Neighbor of an Afghani
27 Liszt's "La Campanella," e.g.
29 Jerk
30 Make free of impurities or dirt
32 "To ____ World in a Grain of Sand" (William Blake, "Auguries of Innocence"): 2 wds.
34 "The Mod Squad" role
35 Midday
39 Ignore: 2 wds.
42 Dawn Chong and Carruth
43 "The Heart Goes Last" author Margaret
44 Magazine founder Eric
45 Flying machines
46 Gal. or yd.

Down

1 ____-a-brac
2 Swearing-in words
3 Curtis/Lemmon film (with "The"): 2 wds.
4 Meeting
5 "Scent Of A Woman" star
6 Israeli guns
7 "Ahoy ____!"
8 Like some verbs: abbr.
9 Tech. company bigwig
10 Suffix with Caesar
16 Subject for debate
19 Pronounce clearly
20 Turner and others
21 ____ fixe (obsession)
22 River isles
23 ____ blanc (Italian wine grape variety)
24 Greet and seat: 2 wds.
28 Uncontrolled outburst of anger
31 ____ of London
33 "Happy Days" actor Williams
36 Instrument in a wind quintet
37 "American Pie" actress Suvari
38 Spanish men, colloquially
39 Baby food
40 Natl. League city
41 Windhoek's land, once: inits.

191

Across

1 Islamic community
5 In an unctuous fashion
11 By and by
12 "The Reivers" actor Rupert
13 Nickname of tennis player Aaron Krickstein: 2 wds.
15 Garlicky mayonnaise
16 Prehistoric tombs
17 California's Santa ___ Valley
19 Blows away
22 Former Yugoslav leader
26 Kids' game: hyph.
28 Mark left by Zorro?
29 Made tough by habitual exposure
30 Saying: "… big ___ elephant": 2 wds.
31 Mentally acute
35 Apia is its capital
39 Fall short: 3 wds.
41 "Are you" in Andalusia: 2 wds.
42 Jorma Kaukonen album: "Aint ___ Hurry": 2 wds.
43 Smith & ___ pistol
44 No longer secret

Down

1 DDE's alma mater
2 Monolithic Polynesian statues
3 1960s–70s Italian P.M.
4 Methodical examiner
5 Scottish expression of surprise
6 Classic Camaro: inits., hyph.
7 "The Real" talk show host Love
8 Poly-sci subjects
9 Future ABA member's hurdle
10 Hungers
14 Skin problem
18 Old laborers
19 Sighs of contentment
20 Recording device, briefly
21 County in Idaho
22 Fast-moving waves
23 Suffix with catch or cash
24 Simple shirt
25 Gave the go-ahead
27 Enzyme that breaks down genetic material
30 Capable of: 2 wds.
31 Merganser
32 Bring on
33 Enzymes' suffixes
34 Certain Internet feeds, initially
36 King of beasts' crowning glory
37 Caen's river
38 "American Heist" costar
40 Barbarian

192

Across

1 Milan opera house: 2 wds.
8 Internet protocol, initially
11 Country, capital Quito
12 Long period of time
13 "Getting to Know You" musical: 4 wds.
15 Yak's home
16 Acknowledge to be true, with "to": 2 wds.
17 Some shoe sizes
18 Garden pests
19 Rapping Dr.
20 Consisting of large grains or particles
21 Spanish toast
22 Juicy information
24 Built in a plant: abbr.
27 Types
28 Fit as a fiddle
29 "Alas, to no ___ ..."
30 Seat of Ward County, N.D.
31 Measure of heat
33 Mine stuff
34 Men of Mexico
35 French seasoning
36 "Keystone Kops" producer

Down

1 Rented
2 More sore
3 Big name in honey: 2 wds.
4 Bakery buys
5 Mine entrance
6 Colleague of Bela and Boris
7 Golden Fleece seeker
8 Menace of comics
9 Little rounded lump or swelling
10 Salon sounds
14 Certificate on a wall, maybe
18 They're underfoot
20 Haphazard
21 Money substitute
22 Harsh
23 Potter's glaze
24 Fertilizer
25 Small piece of cauliflower
26 Dislike
27 Madrid mousers
28 Make a pass at: 2 wds.
30 "Buddenbrooks" author
32 Suffix for jambo or kedge

193

Across

1 Actor LaBeouf
5 Jewish calendar month
11 Nashville is its cap.
12 Composer of the "Israel Symphony"
13 In, on a stamp: abbr.
14 Lovely and delicate
15 Take too much of, briefly: 2 wds.
16 Second-in-command, shortly
17 "___-Dick" (Herman Melville whale)
19 Rhymer's writing
23 Manuscript encl.
25 Expresses agreement
27 Pianist Rubinstein
29 Show with Jean-Luc Picard as the "Enterprise" captain, in fan shorthand
30 Trading
32 Laughing sound
33 ___ Roker (Hannah Montana's bodyguard)
34 Will-___-wisp: 2 wds.
36 Unspecified no.
38 "Hot cross buns, ___ penny, two…": 2 wds.
41 Four-time champion of the Australian Open
44 Kiddies
45 And so on, and so on, for short: 2 wds.
46 Jet set jets, for short
47 Anatomical cavities
48 Give birth to a lamb, old-style

Down

1 Houston ballplayer, to fans
2 Consideration
3 Government duty levied on income: 2 wds.
4 "All work ___ play…": 2 wds.
5 Pendergrass and Riley
6 Requiem Mass word
7 Small piece of anything
8 Layer
9 OPQ followers
10 Suffix with inferior or infidel
18 Adriatic seaport
20 Precisely: 3 wds.
21 Sicilian spouter
22 Catholic title, for short
23 Partially-recognized state of Western Sahara, initially
24 Mars: prefix
26 Certain N.C.O.
28 Roman name for Odysseus
31 Beginner
35 ___-totsy
37 Are, in Argentina
39 Jazz singer Jones
40 PGA part
41 J. J. Pershing's command in W.W. I
42 1960s muscle car, initially
43 Cooling units, for short

194

Across

1 Theater box
5 Christmas tune
10 Lubricate: 2 wds.
12 Alter
13 "___ of Rock 'n' Roll" (Ringo Starr hit of 1976): 2 wds.
14 Belletrist Madame de ___
15 Football player's seat
17 Inventories of injured sports players, intially
18 "___ Carter" (Lil Wayne album)
20 Once upon ___: 2 wds.
22 Restaurant freebie
24 1995 Nobel Prize winner Heaney
27 Manner of speaking
29 'Rawhide' rope
30 Middle Eastern market
32 A hundred sawbucks, briefly: 2 wds.
33 One-celled creature
35 Brit. award
36 Outer: prefix
38 Mole kin
40 "Something to Talk About" singer Bonnie
42 Sporting blades
45 Cacophonous
46 Mimics
47 Japanese company whose name means "three oceans"
48 Leopard's marking

Down

1 Mauna ___, Hawaii
2 Suffix with fact
3 Growth to a worldwide scale
4 Feminine suffix
5 Person handling money in a store
6 Quantity: abbr.
7 Meatloaf song: 4 wds.
8 First-year J.D. student: 2 wds.
9 Cholesterol varieties, initially
11 Former Sec. of Energy Federico
16 Coins: abbr.
18 Chicago daily, for short
19 "The Today Show" co-host Kotb
21 Spring month in Lisbon
23 Good earth
25 Mountain West Conference team
26 Palm starch
28 Outstanding musician
31 President before JAG
34 Geometric figure
36 Historians' concerns
37 "Fame" singer Irene
39 Omar who plays Dr. Foreman on "House"
41 Scotland's Firth of ___
43 Canyon or ranch ending
44 Concorde, e.g.

95

Across

1 Didn't take part, with "out": 2 wds.
6 High: prefix
10 Black Sea port, new-style
11 Early year: 2 wds.
12 2012 movie about a disgraced Detroit cop: 2 wds.
14 Canister
15 Want ad palindrome, initially
16 Small town: abbr.
17 First lady
18 Engine part: abbr.
19 Make bigger, as a photo: abbr.
20 Eggheady sort
22 Applying
24 Like some seals
26 Not the least blowzy
28 Egyptian vipers
32 Bible book before Zeph.
33 German shout
35 Your, in Roma
36 "Just as I thought!"
37 Bath
38 "___ for you"
39 Situations that could suddenly become violent
42 In a suitable manner
43 "Me and Bobby ___"
44 "See" follower in a footnote
45 Gathered silver, among other things

Down

1 Tone down
2 Where disks go, on some computers: 2 wds.
3 High schooler
4 "There ___ tide…": 2 wds.
5 Sulu portrayer George
6 Chemical ending
7 Add yeast
8 Removing
9 Musical composition that evokes rural life
11 Port in eastern Denmark
13 Healthy alternative to snack food: 2 wds.
21 Clinton, e.g.: abbr.
23 "Esto perpetua" is its motto: abbr.
25 Voters' problem
26 "The Prophet" author ___ Gibran
27 W.W. II torpedo ships: hyph.
29 Carefully planned deceptions, slangily
30 Leg wrap for soldiers
31 Dissed, in a way
32 Late labor leader Jimmy
34 SALT concern: hyph.
40 ___-mo
41 "ER" venue

196

Across

1 Oldest technological univ. in America
4 French vineyard
7 Danger in Iraq, initially
8 Hesitant sounds
9 Syr.-Egypt alliance of 1958–61
12 Put on, like comfier clothes
15 Kay Thompson title imp
16 2010 Apple blockbuster
17 Legal defendant: abbr.
18 Make ___ (be a good vendor): 2 wds.
19 Kind of pencil that halts bleeding
22 Alternative to a Maxwell
23 Fashionable brand of apparel
25 Utah metropolis, initially
27 Façade part
30 Impresario Sol
32 Ben-Gurion Airport is its hub: 2 wds.
33 Narrow inlets
34 Run of luck
36 Basically
38 ___ one (very beginning)
39 Wine: prefix
40 Suffix with Ecuador
41 Rap's Dr. ___
42 Johnny Gat in the "Saints Row" video games, Daniel ___ Kim

Down

1 Choirs may stand on them
2 Ball
3 Quirk
4 Certain mushrooms
5 First president of South Korea
6 Certain currency, initially
9 Having no equal
10 "___ of Two Cities" (novel by Charles Dickens): 2 wds.
11 Broncobuster's venue
13 "___ Passes" (Browning poem)
14 "___ for ice cream": 2 wds.
18 Vinegar, for one
20 Fold under
21 Ore suffix
24 Olds-fashioned auto
25 Scintilla
26 Verdi's "___ Miller"
28 Second smallest Teletubby: hyph.
29 Gas used in welding
31 Full of: suffix
34 Ending for joke or mob
35 Fork part
37 Be inattentive

197

Across

1 Founder of New York's Public Theater
5 "The Betsy" author Robbins
11 General Robt.: 2 wds.
12 Saudi ___
13 Mutually linked
15 Training session
16 Dark brown sugar syrup
21 Salad ingredients, briefly
24 "It Must Be Magic" singer ___ Marie
25 Art sch. class
26 "The check's in the ___"
27 "___ Roll" (Big John Patton album): 2 wds.
29 South African monetary units
30 Female hormone
32 Breathing hole
36 Instrument with a rotating perforated roll: 2 wds.
40 Put air into
41 U.S.N. rank
42 Lounger's cover-up
43 Ed.'s request, initially

Down

1 Chest muscles, for short
2 Cream additive
3 Salon job, shortly
4 Outer edge of an area
5 Conforming to Muslim dietary laws
6 Mountain where Noah's Ark landed
7 Mouse cousin
8 Kimono closer
9 Tyler of "The Incredible Hulk"
10 Actor Daniel ___ Kim
14 Cain's nephew
17 Branch of linguistics
18 Actress Young
19 Chisholm Trail town
20 "Do the Right Thing" pizzeria
21 Singer/ songwriter J. J.
22 Parisian ones
23 "Poison Ivy" director Shea
28 1907 Nobel Peace laureate
29 Defendant, at times: abbr.
31 Bridge authority Charles
33 Arthur C. Clarke's "Rendezvous with ___"
34 Swing voters: abbr.
35 Handed-down history
36 Fundraising gp.
37 Pasture
38 Terrier's sound
39 President of the Southern Chinese Republic 1923–5, Sun ___-sen

198

Across

1 Divine name in showbiz: 2 wds.
6 "___ luck!" ("Knock 'em dead!")
11 Kharg Island resident
12 Cremona craftsman
13 Borough boss
14 Free from the influence of alcohol
15 "Should ___ concerned?": 2 wds.
16 Clear (of guilt)
18 Island in the Caribbean
20 Alway
21 Certain camera, for short
22 Van Eyck and Vermeer
23 "Don't laugh!": 2 wds.
26 Actor Astin
27 "___ see it…": 2 wds.
28 Road crew supply
29 Undergo mental anguish
33 Award bestowed by the "Annals of Improbable Research": 2 wds.
35 Most admired, in chat rooms
36 Big Band musician, ___ Miller
37 Old Commodore computer
39 Intermediate, at law
40 Father's Day toast: 2 wds.
41 Mary of "The Maltese Falcon"
42 Play to the back crowd

Down

1 Mock, maybe
2 Japanese-American baseball player Hideki
3 Talker
4 ___-cone (carnival purchase)
5 Amazing or wonderful occurrence
6 Looped rope
7 "Typee" sequel
8 Group of people attractively arranged
9 "The Anvil Chorus" author Shane
10 Drying frames, clotheslines, etc.
17 Heavy fire of artillery
19 NBA part
22 Make one
23 Hunting hounds
24 Showing intense conviction
25 Cut off
26 Bad mark
29 Doubleday of baseball
30 "… ___ say so myself": 3 wds.
31 Restaurant survey company
32 Dodge
34 "Step ___ pets" (animal-friendly palindrome): 2 wds.
38 May honoree

199

Across

1 Galway Bay's ___ Islands
5 Water-soluble gas
11 Make a bundle
12 Psychoanalyst and neurologist Coriat
13 Chauffeured auto
14 Beach breeze: 2 wds.
15 Put out
17 Not bright
18 Wet ground of decomposing vegetation: 2 wds.
23 Love god of Rome
25 Danish architect Jacobsen
26 Be temporarily: 2 wds.
28 Offering to voters
29 Level
30 Cropped photos?
31 Aims for: 2 wds.
33 Lotion letters
36 Critically important
38 Capital of Eritrea
42 Siberian river
43 Toned down
44 Middle of Q.E.D.
45 Tenant
46 Women, slangily

Down

1 Differently-___ (handicapped)
2 "Spider-Man" director Sam
3 University anthem: 2 wds.
4 Glowing sign
5 Nun's title
6 "___ little silhouetto of a man…": 3 wds.
7 ___ an der Thaya, Austrian town
8 Pascal-based language
9 "___ won't be afraid" ("Stand by Me" line): 2 wds.
10 Go astray
16 Where G.I.s get mail
19 Barber's supply
20 Woman's garment
21 Mich. neighbor
22 "Isn't that somethin'?"
24 Adult female horse
26 Bureau of the Treasury Dept.
27 102, to a Roman
28 In ___ (undisturbed)
30 Ceremonial procession
32 Stony hillside
34 ___ Games
35 Shoes without heels
37 Sheet music character
38 Jewish org. founded in 1913
39 Take action against
40 D.C. United's org.
41 Singer Green and others

200

Across

1 À la mode
5 Purple flower
9 Capital of the Liguria region of Italy
11 At attention
12 Alloy used in the making of scientific instruments
13 CB, for one
14 National treasury
16 Sea plea, initially
18 Metal shelf at the side of a fireplace
19 Break down, in a way
20 Letter before kappa
22 Amazon valley people
24 Fine dinnerware
26 Because
29 Crux
31 "Holy cow!"
32 Part of a dish's name: 2 wds.
34 Brief part of the weekend
36 Excited activity
37 Fast dance of the 1940s
40 Eastern church member
41 ___ dhu, ceremonial Scottish dagger
44 British lockups
45 British coins
46 Teen affliction
47 Hasenpfeffer, e.g.

Down

1 Special effects used in "Avatar," e.g.
2 Egg warmer
3 Inquiry into questionable activities
4 Gently persuade
5 "Green Zone" setting
6 Element that loses electrons in a redox reaction: 2 wds.
7 Less welcoming
8 Level
10 Bow
11 Antarctic volcanic peak
15 Angry
16 Order to attack, with "on"
17 "___, That Kiss" (1931 song)
21 Ms. DiFranco
23 ___-eyed
25 Pluses
27 Jerk
28 Japanese capital, once
30 Gob
32 Plant also known as bugle
33 Physics lab device, for short
35 0.5 fl. oz.
38 Bunch of bunk
39 Luau strings
42 Highest possible card in a flush
43 "What's ___?"

201

Across

1 ____ Scrimgeour, Harry Potter character
6 Megalopolis with about 30 million people, for short
11 Turtle Bay VIP: 2 wds.
12 Bid the bed adieu
13 Fraser of tennis
14 Disney film set in ancient China
15 Certain candy manufacturer
17 City in George R. R. Martin's "A Song of Ice and Fire"
18 "I Have a Dream" monogram
20 Knocker's announcement: 2 wds.
22 Soprano Farrell
24 Peak or tip: prefix
27 Wax signets
28 "The Stranger Manual" poet Rosemurgy
29 Vandals
30 Milk protein
31 Los ____, Calif.
33 U.K. mil. award
34 Ginger drink
36 Tony, e.g.
38 Daphne's sitcom hubby
40 Toot one's own horn
43 Nice girls?
44 Answer to "Are not!": 2 wds.
45 Old hat
46 Swedish cars

Down

1 Score on the diamond
2 A, in French
3 Costar in the 2011 movie "Unknown": 2 wds.
4 River that feeds the Ubangi
5 Homo sapiens, for one
6 Greek island close to western Turkey
7 Sch. in Tulsa, Oklahoma
8 Got facts and statistics together: 2 wds.
9 Have ____ in the matter: 2 wds.
10 Eye part
16 Big box of cigs: abbr.
18 Coordinate
19 Stead
21 "Underboss" author Peter
23 "Lohengrin" soprano
25 "How the Other Half Lives" author Jacob
26 Prefix with -phile
28 Yellow-rinded melons
30 Unnerve
32 Café cup
34 French donkeys
35 Cheery tune
37 Downey of "Touched by an Angel"
39 Electrifying swimmer
41 Kind of story
42 How-____ (guides)

Solutions

1

R	E	C	T	O	■	S	E	R	B	S
S	N	O	O	P	■	O	X	I	D	E
V	E	L	D	T	■	N	A	C	R	E
■	■	L	O	I	S	■	M	O	M	A
U	S	A	■	C	O	S	I	■	■	■
S	O	P	H	■	B	O	N	B	O	N
C	A	S	A	S	■	L	E	O	N	A
G	R	E	W	U	P	■	R	B	I	S
■	■	T	E	A	K	■	O	N	T	■
T	A	N	H	■	R	E	P	L	■	■
A	S	S	O	C	■	E	F	I	L	E
R	E	F	R	Y	■	L	U	N	G	E
P	A	W	N	S	■	Y	I	K	E	S

2

A	L	A	R	■	E	J	E	C	T	A
B	A	N	E	■	V	A	L	U	E	S
C	O	N	T	R	I	B	U	T	E	S
■	■	■	E	Y	E	L	I	D	■	■
■	R	A	P	S	■	■	R	E	P	A	Y
R	E	L	E	T	■	U	S	A	G	E
O	R	E	■	■	■	■	■	L	A	W
B	U	R	S	A	■	W	I	M	P	S
E	N	S	U	E	■	E	R	I	E	■
■	■	■	B	R	A	V	O	S	■	■
F	U	N	D	A	M	E	N	T	A	L
A	G	O	U	T	I	■	E	R	N	E
T	H	R	E	E	D	■	D	Y	A	D

3

A	R	M	O	R	■	C	I	G	A	R
A	M	A	D	O	■	H	U	R	T	S
A	N	N	A	S	■	I	M	A	C	S
■	■	A	S	S	A	D	■	H	O	S
C	O	G	■	I	R	E	N	A	■	■
E	X	E	U	N	T	■	A	M	O	N
P	E	S	C	I	■	S	I	C	K	O
E	N	O	L	■	A	L	F	R	E	D
■	■	M	A	U	N	A	■	A	D	E
G	B	E	■	D	E	S	A	C	■	■
L	A	H	T	I	■	H	I	K	E	S
U	C	O	N	N	■	E	D	E	N	S
T	O	W	N	E	■	R	A	R	E	R

4

C	H	A	P	E	L	■	■	C	L	E
S	O	L	A	C	E	■	P	A	I	D
S	I	E	R	R	A	■	O	P	I	E
■	■	■	T	U	R	N	T	A	I	L
O	I	L	Y	■	N	I	A	■	■	■
C	R	E	P	T	■	S	T	O	L	I
H	A	V	O	C	■	E	O	S	I	N
S	N	I	P	E	■	I	B	E	A	M
■	■	■	P	L	S	■	E	S	M	E
D	A	T	E	L	I	N	E	■	■	■
U	S	E	R	■	D	O	T	T	E	D
P	E	C	S	■	E	I	L	E	E	N
E	T	H	■	B	R	E	A	K	S	■

Solutions

5

	R	A	C	E		S	O	L	E	
S	E	R	R	A		M	A	A	M	S
T	H	A	T	S	B	E	T	T	E	R
O	A	R		Y	U	L		E	R	A
P	B	A		O	Y	L		L	I	S
A	S	T	I	N		I	D	Y	L	
		I	T	S	N	O				
M	I	N	H		G	I	D	D	Y	
D	O	N		E	E	S		E	R	E
A	N	S		E	X	A		A	I	N
D	A	I	L	Y	P	L	A	N	E	T
E	D	D	I	E		T	E	N	S	E
	S	E	I	S		S	C	A	T	

6

	A	M	A	S		A	U	R	A	S
O	R	A	N	T		S	L	I	D	E
P	R	I	O	R		C	E	D	A	R
T	I	N		A	A	R		I	G	A
I	V	E		T	A	E		N	E	C
C	A	L	C		H	A	N	G		
S	L	O	P	E		M	E	S	A	S
		B	A	S	S		T	H	R	A
A	B	S		T	A	R		O	I	L
G	E	T		A	B	E		T	Z	U
A	N	E	N	T		U	N	G	O	T
V	E	R	N	E		P	R	U	N	E
E	S	S	E	S		S	A	N	A	

7

R	A	S	E		A	C	T	O	N	E
A	R	U	G		V	O	Y	E	U	R
R	I	G	G		U	N	P	O	T	S
A	D	A	H		L	G	E			
	R	E	E	S		B	B	L	S	
R	E	L	A	X	E	S		O	I	L
E	R	O	D	E		H	A	R	P	O
A	G	A		C	O	M	E	N	O	W
R	O	F	L		S	O	R	T		
		Y	R	S		I	O	L	A	
S	A	N	S	E	I		A	R	Y	L
R	A	N	O	F	F		L	U	R	E
S	H	E	L	T	Y		S	N	E	E

8

B	A	S	I	C		A	D	E	A	D
D	I	T	K	A		B	O	F	F	O
A	D	R	E	P		I	N	F	O	R
Y	E	A		S	W	E		L	U	M
S	S	I		T	A	S		O	L	A
	G	L	A	D		A	R	O	N	
C	O	H	A	N		C	L	E	F	T
H	U	T	T		M	O	E	S		
A	T	F		O	M	M		C	W	M
U	V	A		R	I	P		E	R	Y
C	O	C	O	A		O	M	N	I	S
E	T	E	X	T		R	E	C	T	O
R	E	D	Y	E		T	W	E	E	N

Solutions

9

W	E	B		A	D	O		D	I	M
A	T	E		H	I	M		E	D	O
T	U	A	T	A	R	A		L	O	P
T	I	M	E		E	N	S	I	L	E
			A	S	C	I	I			
A	V	O	C	E	T		D	A	M	P
B	A	T	H	E		A	E	G	I	S
A	N	T	I		A	L	K	A	L	I
			N	I	S	E	I			
C	O	I	G	N	S		C	A	F	E
A	R	C		C	U	C	K	O	L	D
N	E	O		U	M	P		N	A	G
E	O	N		S	E	A		E	K	E

10

E	G	B	D	F		B	A	N	D	O
S	A	R	D	I		A	L	E	A	N
P	R	E	E	X	I	S	T	E	N	T
I	G	A		T	R	I		D	I	I
E	L	S		U	A	L		T	E	M
D	E	T	E	R	S		I	O	L	E
			D	E	C	A	F			
P	C	P	S		I	S	A	A	C	S
U	L	E		R	B	H		S	H	E
T	I	T		E	L	A		S	O	N
S	Q	U	A	R	E	M	E	A	L	S
C	U	L	P	A		E	D	I	L	E
H	E	A	R	N		D	A	L	A	I

11

D	E	M	O	B		C	A	C	H	E
S	P	A	N	O		O	B	E	S	E
M	E	G	A	N		O	R	R	I	S
S	E	N		E	R	N	I	E		
		E	R	D	O	S		A	D	E
F	U	T	U	R	E		S	L	E	D
U	N	I	T	Y		S	L	A	S	H
M	U	C	H		S	K	U	N	K	S
E	M	F		W	E	I	R	D		
		I	N	A	L	L		M	I	A
P	L	E	A	D		L	A	I	R	S
S	O	L	I	D		E	C	L	A	T
S	A	D	L	Y		T	A	K	E	R

12

G	A	S		C	S	S		S	A	P
O	B	E		O	T	O		T	D	S
O	I	L	L	A	M	P		I	I	S
F	E	L	I	X	T	H	E	C	A	T
		E	E	E		I	N	K		
A	U	R	A	S		A	V	I	A	N
N	T	S	B			E	N	Y	O	
S	A	M	O	S		A	N	G	S	T
		A	V	A		B	O	P		
F	O	R	E	V	E	R	M	O	R	E
A	C	K		E	R	O	S	I	O	N
C	H	E		M	E	A		N	U	N
T	O	T		E	S	D		T	E	A

Solutions

13

```
S P I T . . . C R E O N
P O L O . . G H E T T O
O W L S . . L I G H T S
I D A H O A N . . . . .
L E T . . I M A G I S M
. R E I N . . . A G U E
S K A N K . B L U N T .
P E S O . . A L A S . .
A G E N D A S . N T H .
. . . . . I N S H O R E
C A V O R T . A D O S .
O R A N G E . W O K S .
S P R E E . . K N E E .
```

14

```
B I B . . U N W E P T
O P E D . N O O N E S
O S S O . C H O O S E
M A P U T O . . . . .
. . A G E N A . B O S
O N T H E Q T . R K O
N O T Y O U R C A L L
D R E . F E E L S A D
E A R . F R A U S . .
. . . . A T E A S E .
I N A T U B . I R A E
F O R M A L . N D A K
A D M I R E . S R S .
```

15

```
I T S N O . L A M S .
N E N E S . N I P A T
B E A U T I F U L L Y
O P P . E N L . O I L
R E P R O V E . M B E
N E Y O . I R A B U .
. . . I C O S A . . .
. S I S A L . R O D E
L O N . M A K E M A D
U S D . E T A . E R I
C O U N T E R P A R T
R O C C O . M A R I E
E N T R . . A H A N D
```

16

```
A N D N O . E M E R Y
M O R E L . S A D I E
S W I M S . T H I G H
O I L B E A R I N G .
. L U N G E . . . . .
D E B T . R E D T O P
U M I A K . T O O L E
O U T L A Y . G L A D
. . R U E H L . . . .
. D O N A L L O G U E
S A J A K . L U A N N
S H A M U . A S T O N
E L I E L . S E E S A
```

Solutions

17

```
G E N I C █ P A C S █
A B A S H █ R E R U N
N O R M A █ I F I D O
E L K █ I T N █ P S T
F I S H N E T █ P I T
█ █ A R T I C L E I
█ G E R E █ N L E R
F A N D A N G O █
I B M █ C O P Y C A T
N R A █ T S R █ E P I
N I S E I █ E W E L L
Y E S N O █ S A L U T
█ L E A N █ S L O S H
```

18

```
A L G A █ █ A G A S
T H E R O D █ D U L Y
H O O T I E █ D A T S
█ R E L I T █ R A T
R I G █ Y O K E D █
E L E C █ N O K I D S
T E C H S █ S E A R S
S A L A A M █ S N A G
█ O T R A S █ A G T
F L O █ I M E A N █
R E N T █ A L I G H T
O D E R █ S A T E E N
M A Y E █ █ S L A T
```

19

```
S P E S █ F O C H
M I N H █ G O T M A D
E T T U █ U N I D L E
W H I T E N █ O R L E
█ R A M S E S █
E V E █ E A S E F U L
D I T █ T N T █ O L A
W A Y S I D E █ R M N
█ I C A R U S █
A H O T █ M S T A R S
M E D I U M █ I K E A
A L O N S O █ L E N I
█ I M S O █ E S A S
```

20

```
G A M U T █ D A R E
A C U T E █ E C O L E
R E L A X █ B R Y C E
C R T █ A M A █ A I L
O B I █ S T U █ L D S
N I N O █ A C T H
█ C A L C █ H E I R
█ T S A R █ N G O S
P S I █ B A Y █ H O C
E L O █ O F A █ N T H
D A N N O █ W H E L M
I V A N S █ P A S E O
█ E L E E █ S Y S T S
```

Solutions

21

U	S	D	T	■	R	A	T	T	A	T
R	H	E	O	■	E	N	R	A	G	E
D	I	A	N	■	A	N	I	M	A	L
U	N	T	I	T	L	E	D	■	■	■
■	H	O	O	T	■	E	E	L	S	
H	A	T	■	L	Y	I	N	G	I	N
E	E	R	I	E	■	S	T	O	M	A
F	R	A	C	T	A	L	■	T	O	G
T	Y	P	E	■	D	E	L	I	■	
■	C	L	O	S	E	S	E	T		
M	E	M	O	I	R	■	E	T	C	H
E	V	O	L	V	E	■	D	I	R	E
T	E	N	D	E	R	■	S	C	U	M

22

■	S	O	A	P	■	H	A	U	L	S
C	A	N	E	R	■	A	L	G	E	R
A	L	E	R	O	■	R	O	L	E	S
P	A	K	I	S	T	A	N	I	S	■
■		E	Y	E	R	S	■			
A	S	A	S	■	D	E	O	D	A	R
A	E	S		■		O	A	S		
E	A	S	I	N	G	■	C	H	A	S
■		S	E	E	M	S	■			
	T	W	O	A	T	A	T	I	M	E
S	H	A	L	T	■	R	O	M	A	N
T	A	R	D	E	■	T	R	A	C	E
P	I	P	E	R	■	S	E	S	S	

23

R	H	O	D	A	■	T	A	T	U	■
E	A	S	E	L	■	O	L	I	N	S
M	R	M	O	O	N	L	I	G	H	T
I	D	O	■	O	I	D	■	R	U	E
T	I	N	A	F	E	Y	■	I	R	T
S	T	D	S	■	T	O	A	S	T	S
■	A	B	Z	U	G	■				
M	E	S	S	R	S	■	R	A	M	S
A	V	A	■	E	C	L	O	G	U	E
Y	E	P	■	E	H	S	■	N	N	E
S	N	O	O	Z	E	A	L	A	R	M
T	E	R	S	E	■	T	O	T	O	E
■	D	S	O	S	■	S	P	E	E	D

24

R	S	T	■	L	A	C	■			
A	P	O	■	A	C	H	■	F	D	S
N	A	U	T	I	C	A	■	R	E	A
E	S	T	H	■	U	P	S	E	L	L
E	M	E	R	I	L	■	L	E	T	O
■	N	A	S	T	■	A	Z	A	N	
V	I	S	C	O	U	N	T	E	S	S
O	N	E	I	■	R	E	T	D		
I	R	M	A	■	A	P	E	R	C	U
C	O	B	N	U	T	■	R	Y	A	N
E	A	L	■	F	I	N	N	I	S	H
D	D	E	■	O	O	F	■	N	E	A
■	S	N	L	■	G	S	T			

Solutions

25

H	E	B		K	D	S		P	O	L
A	M	I		E	A	T		R	E	M
M	I	N	T	E	D	I	T	I	O	N
		E	P	O	N	Y	M			
D	A	L	L	A	S	G	R	E	E	N
O	D	I	S	T		S	A	C	R	E
Y	A	N					U	N	M	
O	M	E	G	A		C	A	T	I	E
U	N	D	E	R	T	H	E	S	E	A
	R	E	N	O	I	R				
K	A	I	S	E	R	R	O	L	L	S
A	T	V		T	S	R		E	G	O
S	A	E		T	O	S		R	E	D

26

	S	I	D	E		O	N	O	S	
A	C	C	R	A		W	I	C	C	A
S	H	E	E	T	A	N	C	H	O	R
K	A	A		M	T	G		E	T	H
M	A	G	N	E	T	O		R	I	A
E	P	E	E		A	A	H	S	A	T
		S	T	I	L	E				
F	A	S	T	E	N		A	C	A	D
A	P	P		A	D	I	P	O	S	E
T	R	E		L	E	N		M	C	A
W	I	N	T	E	R	G	R	E	E	N
A	L	C	O	A		A	S	O	N	E
	S	E	R	F		S	A	N	T	

27

L	A	G	O		R	E	C	A	P	
E	A	R	N		I	M	B	R	U	E
B	L	O	O	D	V	E	S	S	E	L
E	T	A		R	E	N		E	R	E
C	O	N	C	O	R	D		N	I	C
			L	I	A		J	I	L	T
	M	R	E	D		B	P	O	E	
M	E	O	W		S	E	E			
A	R	Y		S	U	G	G	E	S	T
M	C	A		M	B	E		V	E	Y
B	U	L	L	E	T	T	R	A	I	N
O	R	W	E	L	L		E	D	N	A
	Y	E	N	T	E		P	E	E	N

28

D	E	R		J	I	G		D	O	S
O	V	E		A	N	O		O	R	E
L	E	A		B	Q	E		U	A	L
A	R	D	U	O	U	S		B	C	S
P	L	E	N	T	I	F	U	L	L	Y
S	Y	M	S		S	A	T	E	E	N
			A	T	T	I	R	E	D	
R	U	N	O	U	T		R	E	N	O
E	N	D	P	R	O	D	U	C	T	S
H	E	W		B	R	I	S	K	E	T
A	S	E		I	I	N		E	S	L
B	C	E		N	A	G		R	T	E
S	O	P		E	L	O		S	S	R

Solutions

29

S	E	G	E	R	■	A	L	E	D	O
O	S	A	G	E	■	D	I	C	E	D
R	O	T	O	G	R	A	V	U	R	E
A	L	O	T	■	O	R	I	A	N	A
■	■	■	I	M	B	E	D	■	■	■
P	H	A	S	E	I	■	■	I	D	E
C	O	N	T	I	N	E	N	T	A	L
S	D	S	■	■	H	I	E	I	N	G
■	■	D	R	O	O	L	■	■	■	■
E	M	B	R	Y	O	■	S	O	B	S
G	I	N	A	N	D	T	O	N	I	C
G	L	A	C	E	■	A	N	E	R	A
O	L	I	O	S	■	P	S	A	L	M

30

B	A	W	L	■	S	A	G	E	S	T
A	C	A	I	■	A	N	O	P	I	A
G	R	I	Z	Z	L	Y	B	E	A	R
S	E	T	A	E	■	■	B	E	N	T
■	■	■	R	E	V	U	E	■	■	■
G	L	A	D	■	O	S	T	L	E	R
P	A	L	■	O	D	E	■	A	G	A
O	C	L	O	C	K	■	A	H	O	Y
■	■	N	A	A	C	P	■	■	■	■
M	A	I	L	■	■	O	P	T	E	D
O	R	N	I	T	H	O	L	O	G	Y
T	E	N	N	E	R	■	E	D	G	E
E	A	S	E	L	S	■	T	O	S	S

31

C	O	P	R	A	■	O	S	I	E	R
F	E	T	A	S	■	C	O	N	D	O
C	R	A	S	H	L	A	N	D	E	D
■	■	P	Y	A	■	A	O	N	E	■
S	E	T	S	■	Y	E	T	■	■	■
O	U	R	■	A	R	R	A	N	G	E
P	R	O	G	R	E	S	S	I	O	N
H	O	T	S	E	A	T	■	N	O	V
■	■	T	A	D	■	D	E	F	Y	■
S	C	A	R	■	E	G	O	■	■	■
C	O	M	I	C	R	E	L	I	E	F
A	R	E	N	A	■	N	O	O	N	E
M	A	N	G	Y	■	T	R	U	E	D

32

R	E	B	A	G	■	A	C	K	E	E
P	R	O	M	O	■	M	A	N	L	Y
G	I	S	M	O	■	A	N	O	S	E
■	■	T	O	P	D	R	A	W	E	R
C	F	O	S	■	E	A	R	L	■	■
O	L	N	■	M	E	N	D	E	R	S
P	O	L	■	A	P	T	■	D	A	T
S	W	E	D	I	S	H	■	G	B	E
■	■	T	O	T	E	■	T	E	E	N
I	N	T	E	R	A	L	I	A	■	■
N	O	U	S	E	■	O	R	B	I	T
E	L	C	I	D	■	D	O	L	C	E
S	A	E	N	S	■	I	S	E	E	A

Solutions

33

```
H E A T ■ C A N C A N
A L L I ■ O T O O L E
I M A G I N A T I V E
G O W E S T ■ A N A D
■ ■ ■ H O N K ■ ■
W E R E ■ R E E F E R
P L A N E T A R I U M
M O W G L I ■ S S R S
■ A K O N ■ ■ ■
T W I G ■ N A B O R S
H I S E M I N E N C E
E M M I E S ■ H E M P
O P E N I T ■ R C P T
```

34

```
R I T T ■ O E I L
A B O I L ■ H E N N Y
M E N L O A D D I N
■ S E E I N ■ O T E
M A I W A S O F ■
A L L S M O R T A L
R U L E R M A H A L
L I E L O W L E A D
■ C A S E R ■ M A S
M S T I N T R O ■
S T O A T E E N I E
G A M M A S O T T O
T R Y A ■ S H O E
```

35

```
L A P A C E ■ B O B
U Z I P A S S E U L
C O N T E M P L A T E
A I N U ■ Y U C C A
S C A R A B ■ T H O R
■ B R U T ■ E M S
R I O G R A N D E
T E C O K R A ■
O V E N ■ A T T A C K
R E C U R ■ A G U E
P R O B A B I L I T Y
O I L S K I N ■ L I E
R E D ■ E N S ■ E N D
```

36

```
P I C O T ■ I N M E ■
O M A R R N E A T H
T A N G O D O N H O
P G A ■ M O R N I N G
I E D ■ P E A ■ F I G
E D I T E D ■ P E C S
■ A U D ■ S A S ■
E S N E A C C T N O
A P B ■ E P H ■ A A A
G R A N D A M ■ T I T
L U C I D ■ U T I L E
E C O L I ■ C H O I R
■ E N S E ■ K E N T S
```

Solutions

37

N	A	S	A	L				O	W	I	E
A	A	H	E	D		A	B	E	A	M	
I	R	O	N	S		H	O	L	T	S	
R	E	V	E		T	O	L	L			
		E	I	G	H	T		Q	B	S	
F	O	L	D	E	R			U	R	E	
I	D	I		T	O	O		A	E	R	
L	E	N		A	K	E	L	A	S		
L	A	G		S	T	A	S	I			
	S	P	R	Y		P	F	C	S		
P	O	N	T	A		D	A	I	L	Y	
A	L	O	E	S		O	N	E	O	F	
M	A	W	R		C	A	D	D	Y		

38

L	A	C		S	P	A		T	A	P	
E	L	A	S	T	I	C		A	L	A	
K	E	R	O	U	A	C		N	O	N	
	T	O	P	F	L	I	G	H	T		
O	P	I	N	E		A	S	S	A	Y	
A	R	E		A	I	L					
F	O	R	G	E	T	M	E	N	O	T	
	E	N	E			A	W	E			
B	R	A	N	D		S	M	I	L	E	
L	E	I	T	M	O	T	I	V			
O	T	T		O	N	E	S	E	L	F	
O	R	C		S	C	A	T	T	E	D	
D	O	H		T	E	L		Y	E	A	

39

D	A	T	E		H	A	R	A	S	S
A	R	E	S		U	S	E	F	U	L
C	O	S	A		M	A	D	A	M	E
E	D	T		R	A	M		R	O	W
		T	A	E	N	I	A			
J	O	U	N	C	E		F	D	I	C
N	O	B	I	D		T	R	I	N	I
R	H	E	T		B	E	E	P	A	T
		A	L	I	C	E	S			
R	T	S		A	L	S		T	P	S
A	W	H	I	R	L		F	I	A	T
V	I	R	A	G	O		A	C	R	E
I	T	S	N	O	W		S	K	I	P

40

S	A	B		P	I	T					
A	G	E		S	T	U	C	C	O	S	
D	O	W	N	T	O	E	A	R	T	H	
A	R	I	O	S	O		N	E	E	R	
T	A	L	K			O	T	A	R	U	
	E	D	I	T	E	D		M	I	G	
		E	A	S	E	O	F	F			
B	A	R		A	E	N	E	I	D		
R	U	M	O	R			Y	L	E	M	
U	T	E	P		P	A	E	L	L	A	
C	O	N	A	N	O	B	R	I	E	N	
E	S	T	H	E	T	E		N	A	E	
			U	S	D		G	D	S		

Solutions

41

R	A	F	T		T	U	P	E	L	O
O	G	R	E		E	V	A	D	E	R
W	A	I	L		R	U	N	O	U	T
A	P	E		O	S	L	O			
N	E	D		F	E	A	R	F	U	L
		C	O	T		S	A	L	S	A
S	W	A	P			M	A	A	M	
O	A	K	U	M		L	A	G		
U	S	E	L	E	S	S		E	B	B
		E	N	I	D		O	R	E	
T	E	N	N	I	S		A	L	A	S
E	R	I	C	A	S		L	E	V	O
N	A	M	E	L	Y		A	T	O	M

42

B	I	B	I		A	M	I	N	U	S
A	C	A	N		R	O	D	E	N	T
H	E	R	O	W	O	R	S	H	I	P
T	R	I	R	E	M	E				
		G	R	A	N	D	S	O	N	
F	L	O	A	T		O	O	M	P	A
L	O	R	N		R	E	P	S		
A	U	D	I	O		A	M	E	S	S
B	R	O	C	C	O	L	I			
			A	C	E	T	A	T	E	
C	A	T	A	S	T	R	O	P	H	E
I	N	A	R	E	A		R	I	A	L
D	A	C	T	Y	L		Y	A	W	S

43

D	S	C		S	R	I		C	S	A
O	R	C		T	E	N		A	W	K
C	O	R	D	O	B	A		R	O	I
		E	L	A	T		R	O	S	
P	E	P	S	I		R	U	I	N	S
E	L	B	E		N	A	N	O		
S	M	A	R	T	Y	P	A	N	T	S
		P	T	A	S		W	E	I	R
Q	U	A	S	I		F	A	S	T	S
A	S	P		L	I	A	R			
T	E	E		P	O	W	E	R	E	D
A	A	R		I	T	N		E	X	E
R	S	S		N	A	S		F	O	P

44

B	A	S	E	M	E	N		M	A	R
I	N	T	R	U	D	E		A	D	O
C	O	U	N	T	Y	C	O	U	R	T
E	M	C	E	E	S		A	M	O	O
P	I	C	S			A	S	A	I	R
S	A	O		T	U	T	T	U	T	S
		E	G	G	O	S				
U	N	C	T	I	O	N		L	O	P
B	O	E	U	F		C	A	R	L	
A	L	L	I		I	N	A	R	E	A
N	O	I	S	E	L	E	S	S	L	Y
G	A	N		D	I	O	C	E	S	E
I	D	E		T	E	N	O	N	E	R

Solutions

45

```
A D O B E . . . O M S
N E B U L A . . C R I P
S I T S A T . . O I S E
A C A I . . O G L A L A
R E I N . . S O N A R
A R N E . F O R A Y S
. . S E U S S .
B A L S A M . C T R S
I M A C S . H E E P
T O D A T E . E A T A
M U I R . L I M P I D
A R E D . O N E O N E
P S S . G S T A R
```

46

```
. G N U S . W A L L A
A R U S H . I N A I D
W O R D O F M O U T H
N O S T R A . A N T E
E V E . N C O . D L R
D E R M . E N T R E E
. Y E L L O W Y
M E S A B I . A B O U
A T C . S F C . A C T
R A H M . T R I S T E
B L O O D S U C K E R
L I O N S . D U E T O
E I L A T . E S T S .
```

47

```
S E P T I C . S O I L
A S I A G O . O N M E
D A N S O N . V E N A
. . G E T S R I D O F
L A P . O U S E .
O B O . M S T A R S
E R N . G E S . D E E
B I G S U R . H I S
. . M A G I . E N E
S C L E R O S I S .
P O O L . O N H I R E
E C C L . D O O V E R
C A K Y . S T P E T E
```

48

```
I B E T . M C D L .
T O M S K . A P R E S
A B B E Y . R O U S E
S B A . R U T . N B A
C L R . A S I . K O L
A E R O . U N E A S Y
. . A F F A I R S .
H O S T E L . G A R B
O R S . N L E . S O A
N A M . C Y S . K O A
O T E R I . T H U M B
R E N I N . S O N I A
. S T A G . . I K E A
```

Solutions

49

C	A	E	N		V	E	G	G	I	E
C	L	X	I		O	S	H	E	A	S
C	A	T	T		O	T	E	L	L	O
L	E	E	R	E	D	A	T			
	N	I	N	O		T	O	M	E	
S	T	U	C	C	O		O	L	E	N
T	H	A					D	T	S	
L	I	T	D		I	A	M	T	H	E
O	N	E	R		T	R	O	I		
	H	E	S	S	E	M	A	N		
A	U	R	O	R	A		S	E	R	A
O	N	I	O	N	Y		H	R	A	P
K	I	N	K	O	S		A	S	W	E

50

A	O	L		D	T	S		
T	R	A	N	S	I	T		C	M	S
P	A	N	A	C	E	A		A	A	H
L	C	D	S		A	T	H	E	N	A
A	L	I	A	S		E	O	S	I	N
Y	E	N		C	O	S	S	A	C	K
	G	R	I	M	I	E	R		
R	E	F	I	N	E	D		S	T	S
E	X	I	S	T		E	M	A	I	L
S	P	E	C	I	E		A	L	G	E
E	A	L		L	E	E	W	A	R	D
E	T	D		L	O	U	R	D	E	S
	A	C	R		

51

F	E	R	R	I	S		K	A	E
R	E	N	E	G	E		D	I	M	S
O	N	S	A	L	E		O	L	I	O
	C	O	M	M	U	N	A	L
P	H	O	T	O	L	A	B	
S	A	N	I		Y	E	L	P	E	D
I	D	I	O	M		S	E	R	B	O
S	I	N	N	E	D		G	I	A	N
	T	R	E	E	L	I	N	E
B	A	S	I	L	I	C	A	
O	D	O	M		C	O	Z	I	E	R
A	D	U	E		E	L	E	V	E	N
R	L	S		R	E	D	S	E	A

52

A	M	A	J		B	R	A	S	S	Y
R	A	Z	E		R	U	S	H	A	T
A	T	U	S		O	B	T	U	N	D
T	H	R	U	W	A	Y		
	E	C	S	T	A	S	Y
R	A	D	I	S	H		M	L	L	E
I	N	E	R	T		G	A	M	U	T
S	K	E	E		M	O	N	A	M	I
C	A	R	S	E	A	T		
	V	R	O	O	M	E	D
B	I	O	P	I	C		R	E	D	O
C	A	L	I	C	O		C	L	I	P
S	T	E	N	T	S		H	O	N	E

Solutions

53

```
A R C H E D   · C U B E ·
M O R E S O   · I N A N ·
A N T I Q U A R I A N ·
· · N U B S · N L E · ·
· M A Z E L T O V · · ·
M I G · E E L I E R ·
G R O U N D W A T E R ·
B O O T E E · E E R · ·
· D E C A P O D S · · ·
H M M · C L A M · · · ·
U N A V O I D A B L Y ·
L E N A · N U R S E S ·
A M Y S · G A S O I L ·
```

54

```
B O O T E D · S T E ·
A R C H A I C · T I P
D E T E R I O R A T E
G L A S S · V E T T E
E S N E · S E P A L S
S E E · C A R O L E ·
· · C R I E S · · ·
· T O O O L D · D S S
C E L L O S · C E C A
A N I O N · S A L O N
N O N R E S I D E N T
O R D · R E T R A C E
E S A · D E E D E E ·
```

55

```
O F I T · B O A S T ·
G I R O · A R R A S ·
H O R S E T R A D E ·
A R I · N T S B · · ·
M I G U E L · Y G O R
· A N S E L · E D A ·
O P T I C · A P T E R
U T E · O M N I S · ·
T A S E · E D U A R D
· · M I N H · H U E ·
A U C T I O N E E R ·
S H E B A · H A H N ·
I F E E L · L D L S ·
```

56

```
S E L L · O B O L · ·
A L O E S · N E R O S
D O U B L E E A G L E
H I D · R X S · A L I
U S E · S I T I N O N
S E R B · S A R A P E
· · A S T R O · · ·
S E D U C E · B M O C
H E R M A N N · I R A
I L E · R C A · Z I N
M I D D L E S I Z E D
S E G U E · A D E N O
· R E G T · I N T R
```

Solutions

57

A	D	I	T	S	■	T	E	N	O	N
D	O	N	O	T	■	R	I	A	T	A
D	E	A	R	E	■	I	N	U	R	N
S	S	S	■	P	C	P	■	S	O	A
■	■	P	H	O	E	B	E	■	■	
S	T	R	E	E	P	■	L	A	C	E
L	E	A	N	N	■	P	I	T	O	N
C	A	N	T	■	B	E	S	E	T	S
■	S	A	S	S	E	S	■	■		
D	A	H	■	O	A	R	■	I	S	L
I	N	O	U	R	■	E	L	L	I	E
N	E	R	V	E	■	S	A	R	T	O
K	S	T	A	R	■	S	N	E	E	S

58

B	I	P	E	D	■	O	R	F	F	■
I	S	E	R	E	■	M	E	R	L	E
C	O	R	R	E	L	A	T	I	O	N
■	■	I	S	P	S	■	E	D	U	C
E	D	O	■	S	A	P	■	G	R	O
A	U	D	I	O	T	A	P	E	■	■
P	O	I	L	U	■	R	A	F	T	S
■	C	A	T	H	E	D	R	A	L	
U	L	T	■	H	A	G	■	E	E	R
S	O	A	P	■	R	O	V	E	■	■
N	O	B	E	L	P	R	I	Z	E	S
R	I	L	K	E	■	I	T	E	R	S
■	E	E	E	S	■	C	A	R	A	T

59

■	M	B	A	S	■	W	E	F	T	S
G	O	U	D	A	■	E	X	E	R	T
E	N	L	A	I	■	B	P	L	U	S
S	O	L	I	D	S	T	A	T	E	■
■	G	Y	R	A	T	O	R	■	■	
C	R	O	■	L	E	T	S	G	O	
G	A	F	F	E	■	D	E	L	A	Y
I	M	F	R	E	E	■	A	M	S	
■	■	A	L	L	T	I	M	E		
■	P	H	I	L	I	S	T	I	N	E
P	A	U	L	I	■	A	R	N	E	L
A	P	E	E	K	■	D	I	T	S	Y
C	A	D	R	E	■	E	P	O	S	

60

S	P	O	O	R	■	M	C	D	L	T
T	E	P	E	E	■	O	R	R	I	S
M	A	I	N	S	Q	U	E	E	Z	E
T	K	O	■	E	U	S	E	■	■	
■	■	N	O	W	I	S	■	N	A	M
■	E	A	S	T	E	R	E	G	G	
L	E	E	T	■	■	O	C	T	O	
C	A	R	Y	G	R	A	N	T	■	
D	N	S	■	N	U	B	I	A	■	
■	■	M	E	L	O	■	R	I	A	
E	A	R	P	I	E	R	C	I	N	G
P	R	O	A	S	■	T	E	N	T	H
H	A	M	A	S	■	S	E	E	S	A

Solutions

61

P	A	G	E	S				I	D	L	E
E	L	R	O	Y			G	L	O	A	M
L	O	E	S	S			E	L	U	T	E
O	T	E			C	P	R		B	R	R
S	O	N			O	R	U		L	I	I
I	F	H	E			A	N	N	E	A	L
			O	N	E	I	D	A	S		
C	O	U	G	A	R			W	A	S	P
R	S	S			R	I	G		W	A	R
A	C	E			W	E	L		B	Y	O
M	A	G	N	I			E	T	U	I	S
B	R	A	G	G			A	B	C	D	E
O	S	S	O				M	A	K	O	S

62

S	O	I	L			B	S	I	D	E	S
U	N	C	A			A	N	N	O	Y	S
R	E	A	M			G	I	G	U	E	S
E	I	L	E	E	N	F	O	R	D		
			S	H	I	F	T				
E	L	P	A	S	O			S	A	N	D
L	A	I						C	H	O	
M	A	N	A		E	N	S	E	A	L	
		T	A	L	I	A					
G	I	B	S	O	N	G	I	R	L		
L	I	G	E	T	I			G	A	N	T
G	N	O	S	I	S			E	G	A	D
S	A	R	T	R	E			D	O	S	S

63

E	T	H	I	C			E	M	B	U	S
B	R	U	N	O			L	O	A	T	H
B	I	R	D	S	O	F	P	R	E	Y	
S	O	L	I			V	I	E			
			C	H	E	N			E	F	T
A	F	F	A	I	R			V	A	L	E
I	L	L	T	E	M	P	E	R	E	D	
M	O	U	E			A	I	S	L	E	S
S	E	X			S	T	E	T			
			D	O	C			M	U	S	E
E	N	L	I	G	H	T	E	N	E	D	
R	U	I	N	G			E	N	D	E	D
A	N	T	S	Y			A	T	O	M	Y

64

U	P	S	A			F	R	I	T	O	
T	E	A	M			R	E	M	I	T	S
A	N	D	A			A	P	A	T	H	Y
H	T	M	L			N	O	T	I	O	N
			O	I	N	K	S				
S	A	V	E	M	E			I	A	L	
D	R	I			E	X	S		N	E	G
S	T	E			C	H	U	F	F	S	
			I	H	O	P	E				
R	O	W	E	N	A			R	C	A	S
O	N	E	T	O	N			O	T	T	O
Z	A	F	T	I	G			A	E	R	Y
		S	T	A	L	E			R	D	A	S

Solutions

65

S	L	E	E	V	E	S			
I	I	N	S	I	S	T		L	B	O
D	E	F	A	L	C	A	T	I	O	N
E	R	R		E	D	E	N	I	C	
S	N	A	P	S		T	R	E	N	D
	E	N	A	C	T		S	I	G	S
		C	R	I	C	K	E	T		
E	C	H	O		P	I	L	E	S	
R	A	I	L	S		M	Y	M	A	N
U	P	S	E	T	S		V	I	A	
P	R	E	D	I	C	A	M	E	N	T
T	I	D		P	A	L	E	T	T	E
			E	N	G	R	O	S	S	

66

C	O	B	B			T	O	C	K
L	A	U	R	I	E		E	L	H	I
E	S	T	A	T	E		E	N	G	S
	T	U	C	K	I	N			
R	W	E		H	S	T		B	R	O
A	R	R	A	Y		S	K	E	A	N
D	E	C	A	F		M	A	L	I	C
I	N	U	R	E		Y	I	E	L	D
I	S	P		E	A	T		A	S	S
			S	T	R	U	N	G		
A	G	F	A		G	R	O	U	S	E
B	A	L	T		O	N	E	E	A	R
S	N	U	B			L	R	O	N

67

I	M	B	E	D	S			A	R	C
C	O	U	L	E	E		S	E	A	R
I	N	S	A	N	E		E	R	S	E
E	A	T	S		S	P	L	I	C	E
S	C	U	T			O	F	F	A	L
T	O	P	I		B	E	R	Y	L	
			C	H	U	T	E			
	G	O	B	A	D		P	A	L	L
C	O	R	A	L		R	O	U	E	
H	O	B	N	O	B		O	R	C	S
A	V	I	D		A	B	A	T	I	S
S	E	T	S		L	O	C	A	T	E
M	R	S		M	A	H	L	E	R	

68

A	W	S		M	E	S			
R	O	T		T	W	O		A	W	L
C	O	R	O	N	E	R		W	I	E
A	L	I	D		S	E	L	E	N	A
D	E	P	O	T			B	I	E	N
E	N	C		B	I	S	O	N	S	
			A	B	S	C	E	S	S	
	P	R	O	P	E	R		P	O	R
N	A	T	S			S	E	I	N	E
A	T	O	N	A	L		P	R	E	F
P	H	O		F	E	R	T	I	L	E
E	O	N		A	A	A		N	O	R
		R	K	O		G	T	S

Solutions

69

H	O	P	I	N	■	■	J	A	D	A
O	N	L	O	A	N	■	E	L	O	N
R	E	E	C	H	O	■	A	I	R	E
A	G	A	■	■	T	E	N	S	E	■
■	■	S	U	S	A	N	S	■	■	■
I	N	A	M	E	S	S	■	P	S	S
S	O	N	A	R	■	U	S	L	T	A
O	U	T	■	E	A	R	H	A	R	T
■	■	S	N	E	E	R	Y	■	■	■
■	A	D	L	E	R	■	■	G	D	P
S	W	E	E	■	I	N	D	O	O	R
P	E	L	E	■	E	U	R	E	K	A
F	E	A	T	■	■	B	E	R	E	T

70

F	E	R	D	E	■	A	S	A	L	L
A	N	N	U	L	■	W	E	R	E	A
D	A	R	E	S	S	A	L	A	A	M
■	■	T	E	T	R	■	M	D	A	■
D	A	B	■	S	A	E	S	■	■	■
I	D	O	L	■	T	O	A	R	M	S
P	A	R	A	D	E	F	L	O	A	T
S	H	A	R	I	S	■	E	T	R	E
■	■	D	S	M	S	■	O	K	S	■
R	A	F	■	M	A	H	I	■	■	■
A	B	O	M	I	N	A	T	I	O	N
H	A	N	D	S	■	L	O	B	B	Y
M	A	T	T	S	■	L	O	O	S	E

71

G	I	L	T	■	■	S	T	A	T	S
A	R	O	S	E	■	L	E	R	O	I
S	E	D	A	N	■	C	A	I	R	N
■	■	E	R	E	B	■	M	E	A	N
A	H	S	■	S	O	A	S	■	■	■
R	I	T	A	■	A	C	T	S	A	S
T	R	A	D	E	■	H	E	A	R	A
S	T	R	A	T	I	■	R	U	I	N
■	■	M	A	D	D	■	T	A	D	■
B	E	L	S	■	S	A	D	E	■	■
A	R	E	A	L	■	T	E	R	M	S
N	E	A	L	E	■	S	A	N	A	A
A	S	N	E	W	■	R	E	A	R	■

72

O	R	C	■	S	N	L	■	■	■	■
M	O	O	■	E	N	E	■	C	B	S
I	N	N	■	S	E	T	F	R	E	E
T	E	T	E	S	■	T	I	A	R	A
S	E	E	N	I	T	■	L	S	T	S
■	■	M	L	L	E	■	O	H	I	O
S	E	P	■	E	N	D	■	L	E	N
A	L	O	W	■	P	E	N	A	■	■
Y	O	R	E	■	M	A	G	N	E	T
S	P	A	I	N	■	R	O	D	E	O
T	E	R	R	A	C	E	■	I	L	S
O	R	Y	■	P	O	S	■	N	E	C
■	■	A	G	T	■	■	G	R	A	■

Solutions

73

H	A	S	A	■	■	B	A	B	E	L
I	L	E	S	■	■	A	L	O	A	D
S	O	P	H	■	B	I	S	O	N	S
S	E	A	T	B	E	L	T	■	■	■
■	■	R	O	A	N	■	O	L	A	S
P	B	A	N	D	J	■	N	A	M	E
E	A	T	■	U	A	R	■	V	A	I
N	C	O	S	■	M	O	R	A	S	S
N	O	R	W	■	I	T	A	L	■	■
■	■	■	A	M	N	E	S	I	A	C
L	E	N	N	Y	S	■	H	E	M	O
A	R	I	E	S	■	■	A	R	O	O
C	O	M	E	T	■	■	D	E	N	T

74

S	I	B	S	■	S	I	R	E	N	S
A	T	O	E	■	E	T	A	L	I	A
B	E	L	T	■	S	A	V	A	N	T
U	S	E	R	B	A	S	E	■	■	■
■	■	■	A	A	M	■	S	C	A	R
C	A	S	T	L	E	S	■	I	S	O
E	R	R	E	D	■	C	A	N	I	T
C	C	I	■	S	T	R	E	E	T	S
A	S	S	T	■	H	A	R	■	■	■
■	■	■	O	N	E	P	I	E	C	E
L	A	D	D	E	R	■	A	L	O	G
A	R	I	O	S	E	■	L	E	N	I
R	O	O	S	T	S	■	S	A	G	S

75

R	E	N	A	■	■	O	B	E	S	E
E	L	E	V	S	■	H	O	S	T	S
A	V	I	E	W	■	M	O	T	E	T
C	E	L	■	E	N	S	N	A	R	E
T	R	A	D	E	R	■	B	E	E	■
■	■	R	E	T	A	P	■	L	O	M
B	A	M	B	I	■	A	M	I	S	S
E	R	S	■	E	L	S	E	S	■	■
S	S	T	■	A	T	T	H	A	T	■
T	E	R	R	A	C	E	■	M	G	B
I	N	O	U	R	■	O	P	E	R	A
L	I	N	D	A	■	N	I	N	E	R
L	O	G	I	N	■	R	T	E	S	■

76

A	P	O	R	T	■	S	L	A	P	■
S	H	U	S	H	■	T	I	G	E	R
P	A	R	T	I	C	I	P	A	T	E
I	S	M	■	S	H	R	■	S	I	E
R	E	A	D	I	E	R	■	S	T	S
E	I	N	E	■	E	U	B	I	E	■
■	■	C	A	R	P	E	■	■	■	■
■	A	G	I	R	L	■	E	D	A	M
A	P	I	■	C	E	M	B	A	L	O
U	P	A	■	H	S	I	■	R	E	V
R	E	N	A	I	S	S	A	N	C	E
A	A	N	D	E	■	E	R	A	T	O
■	R	I	A	S	■	R	A	Y	O	N

Solutions

77

A	S	P	S			I	C	E	A	G	E
P	L	A	T			M	O	R	L	E	Y
S	A	R	I			P	U	R	P	L	E
E	V	A	N	G	E	L	I	S	T		
			S	T	O	L	E	N			
G	R	I	S	T			E	G	R	E	T
M	A	T						E	R	A	
T	H	E	S	E		F	I	V	E	R	
			E	N	C	A	S	E			
	S	A	C	C	H	A	R	I	N	E	
M	O	N	R	O	E		A	L	O	E	
E	A	T	E	R	S		E	L	U	L	
W	R	I	T	E	S		L	E	N	S	

78

P	A	W	P	A	W		S	H	E	M
A	S	H	A	M	E		A	A	R	E
O	L	I	V	E	S		T	R	A	D
		T	E	N	T	D	R	E	S	S
B	E	E		S	E	R	A			
A	D	S			R	E	P	A	S	T
D	I	E		D	N	A		S	O	A
S	T	A	T	E	S		I	D	O	
		H	E	A	L		S	A	S	
T	A	K	E	S	H	A	P	E		
A	B	E	S		A	M	E	E	R	S
L	A	N	E		R	A	D	I	O	S
A	T	T	S		A	S	I	T	I	S

79

L	A	R	A	S		S	H	A	R	P
A	L	E	N	E		E	E	L	E	R
S	T	A	G	E	M	A	N	A	G	E
T	O	C		K	A	L		M	A	L
L	O	T	S		R	E	T	E	L	L
A	N	O	N		K	G	B			
P	A	R	E	E		S	O	S	A	D
		R	N	R		N	E	U	R	
D	O	N	T	G	O		E	S	S	E
O	N	O		R	B	H		S	T	A
F	I	T	T	O	B	E	T	I	E	D
O	N	E	I	S		A	M	O	R	E
R	E	D	O	S		L	I	N	E	D

80

A	B	E	D		C	H	A	K	R	A
R	A	V	I		E	I	L	E	E	N
A	C	E	S		N	T	E	S	T	S
N	O	E	S		T	A	P			
	N	E	N	E		H	A	L	L	
S	A	S	S	E	R		S	L	O	E
C	E	L		A	F	C		E	D	A
A	R	E	S		I	S	S	U	E	S
B	O	R	E		E	T	A	T		
		D	B	L		G	I	G	S	
D	E	L	E	A	D		G	A	O	L
S	T	E	R	N	E		E	N	T	R
L	O	O	S	E	R		D	S	O	S

Solutions

81

```
M C Q ■ B E D ■ R A D
C R U ■ A D E ■ O L E
G E A R S U P ■ L I P
E A R N ■ ■ P A L E O
E S T A B ■ ■ B E N S
S E E ■ I M M E R S E
■ ■ R A T I T E S ■
F E S T O O N ■ K E S
R A T A ■ ■ S H A N A
I R A N I ■ A T T N
E L F ■ O N A D I E T
D E F ■ T A M ■ N R A
■ ■ A L S ■ G O S
```

82

```
D A R E D ■ ■ C N N
R A F A E L ■ S A Y A
T U S S L E ■ A M E S
■ ■ T E A C H E S T
A S S E T ■ A A R ■
G E N R E ■ B R A V A
F R A S ■ ■ A M A T
A S K U P ■ A D A N O
■ E N O ■ S E N S E
N E E D L E S S ■
A N Y A ■ D U E L E D
P R E Y ■ A M R I T A
A Y S ■ E T U D E
```

83

```
M O U S S E ■ U P A T
S N A K E D ■ G A T S
S E E Y O U ■ A L I A
■ ■ P U C E ■ E E R
S H O E L A C E S ■
A T V ■ T O E T A P
S T E P H E N K I N G
S P R E A D ■ N E A
■ S T A G E S E T S
E A L ■ S U G E
T R E E ■ E R R A T A
D I E D ■ S E I S M S
S A P S ■ S T N I C K
```

84

```
S O L A R ■ F L E E T
A R E N A ■ L A D L E
G I A N T P A N D A S
A G R ■ E R B ■ O L S
■ ■ A D E B T
C A G E R ■ Y A H O O
I D I O ■ M A A S
A S S N S ■ R E S T S
■ S L O E S
A L S ■ I D A ■ O M S
W O U N D E D K N E E
A N N I E ■ D O O N E
D E S K S ■ S O R T S
```

85

```
G I O T T O ■ B A G S
S Q U E A L ■ E L E A
A S T R I D ■ L E T S
■ S I N ■ Y A X I S
U R I ■ T B A ■ A N Y
F A D E ■ A L A N ■ ■
C H E E R L E A D E R
■ C R I S ■ U E L E
H R H ■ O A K ■ R A E
Y E A T S ■ A S P ■
P I N A ■ A L M O S T
E N C L ■ B E E P E R
R E E K ■ S L E E P Y
```

86

```
A B E ■ L I S ■ H A B
C A M ■ A L T ■ O C A
T H E A T R E ■ A D D
S T R I K E F O R C E
■ I R E ■ F I S ■
C E L L S ■ I L E T A
B A L I ■ ■ P A I D
S L A N G ■ B A S E S
■ G E E ■ E P A ■
S M A R T A L E C K S
A A S ■ S T I R R U P
D T S ■ T A E ■ O R A
R E E ■ O B S ■ W D S
```

87

```
A R M S ■ S P I E R
D E E P ■ T A R D E
A N T I S O C I A L
S T A T E P E N ■
■ T R I ■ A C A R
D I A L I N G ■ A G O
A T R E E ■ A P A R T
U A E ■ S A T A N I C
B L A H ■ S H U ■
■ A T T E S T T O
U P R O A R I O U S
R I P O N ■ N A T E
L A Y L A ■ G N U S
```

88

```
A D D E R ■ S O D A S
R O I L S ■ P A C T S
A L L E V I A T I O N
B E L G ■ W R Y ■
■ A D A K ■ B R O
A R E N A S ■ O A H U
B E N C H W A R M E R
I B L E ■ R E E S E S
E S S ■ D O S S ■
■ C A N ■ T H I S
E L B O W G R E A S E
D O O N E ■ A I R E R
A B Y S S ■ D A T E S
```

Solutions

89

A	G	E	R			R	A	B	I	N
H	E	X	A		S	T	R	I	V	E
A	R	P	S		W	E	A	S	E	L
B	E	L	T		I	S	M			
		O	A	K	S		I	A	M	S
C	A	S	S	I	S		S	P	A	T
L	X	I		A	C	T		P	A	D
A	L	O	T		H	A	R	A	S	S
M	E	N	E		E	V	E	L		
			S	S	E		D	O	R	S
M	A	S	S	E	S		C	O	O	T
A	T	T	I	R	E		A	S	Y	E
H	O	S	E	A			P	A	S	T

90

A	S	C	A	N			A	B	C	D
L	E	A	F	E	D		S	E	E	A
T	A	R	T	E	R		S	N	O	T
		R	A	R	E	S	T			
S	C	I		D	I	O		S	L	A
P	R	O	M	O		B	E	T	A	S
A	A	N	D	W		S	M	A	C	K
S	I	E	T	E		T	U	T	E	E
M	G	S		L	B	O		E	D	D
			A	L	A	R	M	S		
S	N	A	G		L	I	A	I	S	E
A	I	R	E		L	E	N	D	E	R
B	A	A	S			S	A	E	N	S

91

A	B	C		H	S	T		F	L	A
G	E	O		E	W	E		O	A	S
T	A	N	G	I	E	R		O	R	S
S	U	T	U	R	E	S		L	B	O
		A	R	E	T	E		S	O	O
A	C	C	U	S	E		P	A	N	
B	O	T		S	N	A		A	R	A
N	U	L		T	B	I	R	D	S	
E	R	E		A	H	O	R	A		
G	I	N		M	E	L	O	D	I	C
A	E	S		O	P	I	N	I	O	N
T	R	E		L	O	S		S	T	E
E	S	S		E	T	H		E	A	T

92

L	A	L	A	W		E	R	D	A	
A	R	I	S	E		B	O	C	A	
S	A	N	T	A	M	A	R	I	A	
S	G	T		K	A	N	E			
			A	N	E		M	O	H	S
A	B	S	C	E	S	S		R	I	A
L	E	A	R	S		H	E	A	R	N
M	A	I		S	A	R	A	L	E	E
S	U	D	S		P	E	N			
		A	R	A	W		B	O	A	
D	E	M	O	L	I	T	I	O	N	
A	S	S	T		S	H	A	N	D	
D	E	A	L		H	I	S	S	Y	

Solutions

93

V	E	L	U	M			C	A	P	E	R
A	N	I	S	E			H	O	R	A	S
S	E	G	E	R			I	L	O	S	T
		H	A	V	O	C		C	T	U	
A	T	T	S		S	K	E	E			
T	H	A		D	E	P	O	S	A	L	
O	R	I	B	I		E	N	S	O	R	
E	U	R	A	S	I	A		S	N	O	
		C	R	T	S		P	E	E	N	
P	A	R		R	E	F	E	R			
A	B	A	S	E		A	D	V	I	L	
C	U	F	F	S		T	A	E	B	O	
O	T	T	O	S		E	L	R	O	D	

94

H	A	R	I			A	L	L	N	E	W
I	C	E	S			L	E	O	I	I	I
N	E	H	I			D	E	T	E	S	T
T	H	E	T	W	I	S	T				
		A	M	A	S		I	F	A	T	
C	A	R	E	S	S		E	I	N	S	
O	G	S						N	I	P	
N	E	A	L		M	O	T	E	L	S	
E	R	L	E		E	M	I	L			
			A	S	T	E	R	I	S	K	
A	R	M	P	I	T		A	N	O	N	
S	E	A	E	E	L		D	E	L	E	
S	L	E	D	G	E		E	N	D	E	

95

	A	G	E	S		L	O	R	R	E
	R	A	C	E		E	A	R	E	D
	A	T	A	T		I	T	S	S	O
	M	O	R	T	I	S	E			
		T	E	N		R	A	S	H	
A	S	T	E	R	N		S	H	O	O
L	A	S					S	O	S	
T	R	A	S		A	S	C	O	T	S
A	I	R	E		N	T	H			
	R	A	N	R	I	O	T			
T	O	T	E	M		A	R	L	O	
A	S	A	N	A		T	A	D	A	
B	A	D	E	N		A	C	E	D	

96

B	I	S		G	E	M		S	O	N
A	S	A	R	U	L	E		E	C	O
D	E	V	O	T	E	D		A	H	S
D	E	E	S		C	A	Y	U	S	E
		T	I	T	T	L	E			
A	M	I	N	O	R		N	A	W	S
C	A	M		A	I	S		N	A	L
T	E	E	M		C	U	R	T	S	Y
		D	E	C	R	E	E			
S	A	Y	S	A	H		P	A	C	E
E	L	O		R	A	R	I	T	A	N
R	A	S		L	I	O	N	E	S	S
A	I	T		E	R	B		R	T	E

Solutions

97

E	D	O		E	D	D		N	O	D
D	A	P		S	E	R	R	A	T	E
A	L	E	X	P	K	E	A	T	O	N
M	I	N	E	O		A	I	L	E	Y
		P	R	O	A	M	S			
T	I	O		D	O	E	S	I	N	
W	A	R	T	S	A	N	D	A	L	L
A	L	T	A	I	R		V	E	E	
		V	E	N	I	C	E			
C	I	N	E	S		G	A	T	O	S
O	V	E	R	T	H	E	L	I	N	E
R	E	E	N	A	C	T		M	T	M
D	S	T		S	H	A		E	O	S

98

T	H	A	R		T	R	O	M	P	E
O	E	N	O		R	E	P	A	I	R
I	W	A	S		A	V	A	N	T	I
	L	E	A	P	S		E	T	C	
L	A	Y	S	U	P		D	A	K	
O	A	S		R	E	C				
A	M	T		A	R	R		N	A	B
		E	K	E		I	N	A		
A	S	P		E	S	S	A	Y	S	
T	H	E		R	E	T	A	G		
E	A	T	S	U	P		C	A	B	S
A	R	E	O	L	E		K	R	I	S
M	E	R	G	E	R		S	A	N	T

99

H	A	S	E	K			P	S	S	T
I	L	O	V	E		E	A	M	E	S
H	A	N	E	Y		S	N	E	A	K
O	N	O	N	E	S	T	O	E	S	
		A	D	I	E	U				
S	S	T	S		G	E	T	S	E	T
O	N	S		O	H	M		B	A	S
B	O	A	R	D	S		C	A	T	E
		A	D	A	G	E				
S	A	N	I	T	A	R	I	U	M	
F	I	R	S	T		M	I	T	Z	I
A	N	N	O	Y		U	S	A	I	R
D	E	E	M		T	E	N	S	E	

100

G	S	O	S		L	I	N	G	O	S
O	C	A	T		A	S	M	A	R	A
T	H	R	A	S	H	M	E	T	A	L
C	O	I	N	E	R	S		E	T	E
H	O	N	D	A		S	A	E	S	
A	L	G		C	A	C	T	U	S	
		L	A	R	R	Y				
	M	A	I	T	A	I		D	I	O
B	A	L	D		P	E	R	D	U	
O	R	U		E	K	E	S	O	U	T
A	R	M	T	W	I	S	T	I	N	G
S	E	N	I	O	R		E	D	N	A
T	R	A	C	K	S		E	S	O	S

Solutions

101

S	P	A	C	E			S	H	E	D	S
A	R	E	A	R			L	O	O	I	E
T	O	R	S	I			A	N	N	A	N
S	P	O	T	T	I	N	E	S	S		
		S	A	U	L	T					
O	R	O	N		L	E	T	S	O	N	
B	A	L	E	S		D	O	E	R	S	
S	I	S	T	E	R		L	A	D	A	
			T	E	H	E	E				
	T	A	B	U	L	A	R	A	S	A	
A	E	S	O	P		M	A	G	D	A	
M	A	C	R	O		A	T	L	A	S	
A	L	I	E	N		L	E	E	K	S	

102

	C	O	R	P	S		A	A	R	E
C	E	T	E	R	A		C	R	E	D
N	A	T	I	O	N	S	T	A	T	E
E	S	E		A	A	E		B	I	N
T	E	R	M	S		M	I	L	E	S
		D	S	C		D	I	M	E	S
			R	A	I	S	E			
	B	E	A	S	T		T	A	H	
L	A	S	E	S		P	A	C	E	R
E	R	S		T	A	O		C	R	I
T	R	E	E	S	U	R	G	E	O	N
T	I	N	A		R	E	A	P	E	D
S	E	E	N		A	D	I	T	S	

103

N	O	P	L	A	C	E		A	M	A
A	R	E	O	L	A	E		P	A	C
E	R	A	S	E	R	S		S	T	N
		A	S	P		L	I	T	E	
A	L	A	N		A	R	I	S	E	S
B	A	N	G		L	E	T			
S	A	S	E	S		S	T	O	A	S
		L	A	U		L	I	A	R	
A	S	S	E	T	S		E	L	M	S
B	E	A	S		H	B	O			
A	N	A		M	E	A	N	I	E	S
C	O	B		A	R	S	E	N	I	O
A	R	S		A	S	K	S	F	O	R

104

I	L	L		S	W	A		P	A	C
S	O	A		P	A	K		R	C	A
A	L	T		A	T	E		I	C	C
A	L	I	E	N	E	E		N	E	T
C	O	N	F	I	R	M		C	S	U
S	P	A	R	E	S		B	E	S	S
		M	O	L	O	T	O	V		
B	I	E	N		F	I	N	A	L	E
A	R	R		S	T	E	E	L	I	E
L	A	I		N	E	R	D	I	E	R
L	I	C		A	N	O		A	R	I
A	S	A		R	E	D		N	N	E
D	E	N		E	R	S		T	E	R

Solutions

105

	E	S	T	D		B	R	I	T	T
A	L	I	N	E		L	U	N	A	R
H	I	N	T	S		I	N	D	R	A
E	N	G		C	A	N		U	P	I
A	O	L		E	S	I	A	S	O	N
P	R	E	E	N	S		M	T	N	S
		S	E	D	U	C	E	R		
T	A	P	E		M	A	R	I	S	A
E	D	A	S	N	E	R		A	E	S
M	O	C		O	D	S		L	T	S
P	R	I	V	Y		I	S	I	T	I
E	E	N	I	E		C	O	Z	E	N
R	E	G	I	S		K	L	E	E	

106

D	A	T	E			T	A	P	A	S
A	B	O	M	B		E	N	E	R	O
S	E	R	T	A		S	N	A	I	L
		T	S	L	O	T		N	A	E
I	B	O		D	R	E	W	U		
N	A	I	F		S	E	A	T	A	C
E	L	S	E	S		S	I	G	N	O
S	E	E	R	E	D		T	A	E	L
		S	E	E	N	A		L	G	A
F	E	H		S	A	L	A	L		
E	L	E	N	A		E	M	E	R	Y
A	L	L	O	W		G	O	R	G	E
T	E	L	L	S			S	Y	S	T

107

I	R	O	N		D	E	L	T	A
N	I	N	E		C	E	R	E	A	L
T	E	E	N		A	S	R	A	R	E
S	U	P	E	R	B		O	D	O	N
		I	S	O	B	A	R			
B	E	E		B	A	N	S	H	E	E
A	E	C		U	G	O		U	R	L
D	R	E	S	S	E	D		C	A	F
		A	T	R	I	S	K			
P	O	R	T		O	C	A	S	E	Y
R	E	O	I	L	S		I	T	N	O
E	N	T	R	E	E		D	E	C	K
Z	O	O	E	Y		A	R	L	O	

108

A	H	H		E	W	E			
D	E	A	D	S	E	A		S	E	E
A	B	R	E	A	S	T		H	Y	P
	L	A	I	T		D	O	R	P
A	M	E	R		S	M	O	R	E	S
R	A	Y		B	I	O	N	T	
B	P	S		A	D	S		C	C	I
	T	A	S	E	S		H	D	S
S	A	R	A	H	S		C	A	S	H
A	L	E	A		T	R	O	N	
C	I	E		G	O	I	N	G	T	O
K	A	T		P	R	E	S	E	N	T
		A	Y	N		D	N	S	

Solutions

109

B	E	A	D				E	A	T	S
A	R	G	O	S		A	G	N	E	W
C	R	A	N	E		C	I	G	N	A
K	A	S			P	R	E	S	E	N	T
E	T	S			T	E	Y		L	I	A
R	A	I	N	E	S		O	A	S	T
			S	T	I	E	D	
U	S	M	A		D	V	O	R	A	K
N	E	O		C	U	E		E	R	N
E	A	R	T	H	E	N		E	E	E
A	S	A	H	I		U	P	B	O	W
S	O	L	I	D		P	A	O	L	I
E	N	E	S				S	K	A	T

110

S	A	G	A	N			A	K	I	N
T	A	U	T	E	N		R	I	S	E
N	A	T	I	O	N	S	T	A	T	E
			M	N	E	M	
E	L	V	E	S		E	A	R	P
S	A	D			P	A	N	E	R	A
O	R	A	L	S	U	R	G	E	O	N
S	A	R	A	H	S			C	M	A
	S	A	G	O		A	M	E	S	S
		T	A	P	E	
L	O	T	U	S	E	A	T	E	R	S
A	S	A	S			S	T	R	E	E	T
B	E	S	S			H	O	L	E	R

111

P	E	A	S			F	I	E	F
R	A	C	E	R		B	O	R	E	D
I	R	A	N	I		E	R	I	E	S
I	N	D	I	S	T	R	E	S	S
			L	E	N	T	S
A	S	S	E	R	T		T	A	M	A
A	O	K				T	A	C
E	R	A	T		W	A	S	H	E	R
		U	S	A	G	E
B	A	R	E	H	E	A	D	E	D
A	O	L	E	R		R	A	I	S	E
B	R	I	E	F		S	I	N	C	E
A	N	I	N			R	E	E	D

112

C	A	S	E		O	C	C	U	L	T
R	E	C	S		R	O	A	M	E	R
E	R	A	T		I	S	R	A	E	L
A	I	R	S	P	E	E	D
M	E	S		I	N	C	I	S	O	R
		D	I	N	T		G	O	R	E
A	T	A	L	E		L	A	L	L	Y
B	I	L	L		W	A	N	D
O	N	E	U	N	I	T		I	R	T
		M	E	N	S	W	E	A	R
A	I	R	I	N	G		A	R	N	E
B	R	U	N	E	I		L	O	T	S
A	R	R	E	S	T		E	N	O	S

Solutions

113

```
D I R T Y   ■ A P T T O
I C A R E   ■ C L A R A
N A V E L   ■ L E P E R
A L E X T R E B E K ■
    ■ S A F E S ■
C A S E I N ■ I T C H
A D A M N ■ C A R T E
D O R M ■ B A N Y A N
  ■ D A M O N ■
  B I P A R T I S A N
B O N E S ■ A S O L O
P L I E S ■ T I L E R
S T A L E ■ A S S A D
```

114

```
I F S ■ O N A ■ T O C
S E A M I N G ■ O L E
L E G A L E A G L E S
A L O U S ■ S W E A T
  ■ V E S P E R S ■
A S L E E P ■ N A T O
C T U ■ D Y S ■ T E A
C A N A ■ R A C E R S
  ■ R E S P I R E ■
A T T H E ■ C L Y D E
A L T E R C A T I O N
H E E ■ T O S S P O T
S R S ■ H E M ■ E M O
```

115

```
R A S ■ R A L ■
A T T ■ E R E ■ C C S
M A R T I N A ■ R A N
  ■ I O N E ■ B O R E
T O N Y S ■ W A S T E
R A G ■ T H A T S ■
E T C ■ A R I ■ S I D
  ■ H A T E S ■ E C O
A B E L E ■ T E C H S
R A E S ■ S L A T ■
L B S ■ N O I S I L Y
O S E ■ A I N ■ O Y S
  ■ B E E ■ N E L
```

116

```
L I N E S ■ S P I E L
E N A M I ■ H O N E Y
A S R E D ■ O T O E S
F I R E E A T E R S ■
  ■ G A R B A G E ■
E N T ■ A U N T I E
D I O N E ■ N S Y N C
W A R A C E ■ P E G
  ■ S L E E P E R ■
  C H A I R L I F T S
W H E L P ■ I T A G O
H A I L S ■ O C C A M
O N R Y E ■ T H E S E
```

Solutions

117

```
A L A N . . W A D E R
C E N O . B R U I S E
R E A R . R A R E L Y
O R A T O R I O . . .
. . L O B . T R A P S
A L I N E . H A R T E
B I C . . . . M A I .
A M I G A . C R A S S
S E A O F . I E D . .
. . A R S O N I S T .
G O I T E R . E L H I
A R N E S S . E L A N
N E N E H . S O D A .
```

118

```
C U F F S . R S V P S
O N E A L . Z A I R E
G U A V A . A Y R E S
. S T O P A . S G T S
L E H R . R O T I . .
O D E . B E G O N I A
C T R . I A L . I C C
H O W C O M E . A E R
. E S S A . O S H A .
D O I T . P O L L O .
U N G O T . I L I U M
M A H R E . S A M S A
A S T E R . E S S E N
```

119

```
. A M O R . O C H O .
E R A S E . C H A R D
F I R S T D E G R E E
S A E . A I L . T O A
. . A G L O W . . . .
A M A S S . T A S S O
N A T S . . . G E A R
S T A E L . C E A S E
. . T A R A S . . . .
D H L . M A N . A R M
C O O K E R Y B O O K
I O W A S . O R N O T
. F E T A . U S E D .
```

120

```
T O R R . S N E A K
S N A P S . T O N E R
G A M M A C A M E R A
A P A . B A R . M A I
R A D . E S L . A T T
P R A M . T E N S E S
. . . P S A T S . . .
T E A S E S . C A L E
A U S . E I S . N A M
M G S . T D S . O T O
T E A C H E R S P E T
A N I L E . S E I N E
M E L I S . C A T S .
```

Solutions

121

B	E	A	R	■	■	A	M	A	S	S
B	A	L	E	■	A	R	A	B	L	E
L	S	T	S	■	S	E	N	O	R	A
S	E	E	P	■	H	A	I	■	■	■
■	■	R	O	W	E	■	A	S	A	S
R	U	N	N	I	N	G	■	T	I	A
C	L	A	D	S	■	L	E	A	D	S
P	E	T	■	C	H	E	R	I	S	H
T	E	E	M	■	H	E	R	R	■	■
■	■	■	E	G	O	■	A	C	T	I
S	U	B	A	R	U	■	T	A	R	R
O	P	E	N	E	R	■	U	S	E	E
L	A	S	T	S	■	■	M	E	T	S

122

N	A	S	A	■	A	V	A	U	N	T
A	L	A	S	■	P	I	S	T	O	N
P	O	L	S	■	R	E	P	E	N	T
S	E	T	A	S	I	D	E	■	■	■
■	■	P	I	L	L	■	N	A	A	N
A	Y	E	■	A	F	T	■	U	F	O
C	O	T	■	N	O	R	■	T	A	I
E	Y	E	■	T	O	E	■	O	R	R
S	O	R	T	■	L	A	M	P	■	■
■	■	U	P	S	T	A	I	R	S	■
H	U	R	L	E	D	■	G	L	E	E
A	Z	A	L	E	A	■	M	O	D	E
T	I	M	E	L	Y	■	A	T	O	M

123

A	T	C	■	B	A	M	■	M	A	A
A	R	B	■	E	T	A	■	D	O	C
R	E	E	N	T	E	R	■	S	U	E
P	O	S	E	■	S	L	E	E	T	S
■	■	■	A	C	T	A	S	■	■	■
S	A	B	R	A	S	■	S	A	E	S
A	R	I	E	L	■	M	A	O	R	I
C	A	N	A	■	S	T	Y	L	E	S
■	■	■	S	H	A	N	E	■	■	■
S	T	A	T	A	L	■	R	C	M	P
L	I	B	■	L	A	S	S	O	E	R
R	E	B	■	E	D	A	■	B	E	E
S	A	R	■	R	A	P	■	S	D	S

124

A	T	T	U	■	V	A	S	S	A	R
M	O	E	N	■	I	N	H	E	R	E
A	M	T	S	■	C	N	O	T	E	S
S	E	E	A	F	T	E	R	■	■	■
■	■	A	F	R	O	■	E	L	S	A
I	N	T	E	A	R	S	■	O	A	R
D	E	E	■	N	I	E	■	C	L	I
D	A	T	■	C	A	R	C	A	S	S
O	R	E	L	■	C	A	U	L	■	■
■	■	■	A	I	R	C	R	A	F	T
S	T	E	R	N	O	■	D	R	E	A
H	I	N	G	E	S	■	L	E	A	R
E	X	C	E	S	S	■	E	A	R	N

Solutions

125

	C	R	I	B		S	N	E	A	D
S	H	O	N	E		A	O	R	T	A
T	A	N	K	S		S	T	I	P	E
D	I	S	P	O	S	S	E	S	S	
			A	T	H	O	L			
R	A	N	D		O	O	L	A	L	A
A	A	A		L	P	N		D	A	M
S	E	P	S	I	S		M	A	S	S
		K	O	A	L	A				
	S	T	E	N	T	O	R	I	A	N
A	R	E	W	E		T	O	N	N	E
B	A	T	E	S		T	O	D	O	S
U	S	E	R	S		A	N	S	A	

126

C	R	I	E	S		P	O	S	E	R
H	E	N	N	A		A	V	I	L	A
A	M	I	T	Y		R	E	S	E	T
R	O	T	I	S	S	E	R	I	E	
			T	Y	I	N	G			
S	T	A	Y	E	D		O	M	A	R
S	O	S		S	E	D		A	A	M
S	O	A	R		C	A	N	V	A	S
		A	W	A	R	E				
	A	F	T	E	R	T	A	S	T	E
S	O	L	T	I		G	R	E	E	N
O	N	E	L	S		U	T	T	E	R
P	E	D	E	S		N	O	I	S	Y

127

A	A	H		A	C	U				
S	N	E	E	R	A	T		P	M	S
I	S	A	D	O	R	A		E	A	U
N	E	R	D		R	H	Y	T	H	M
		T	A	T	I		E	E	O	
L	E	T	S	B	E		O	F	N	O
O	R	O		A	R	B		O	I	L
D	O	H	S		P	A	P	U	A	N
	T	E	A		I	M	A	N		
D	I	A	L	O	G		B	T	E	N
A	C	R		S	E	A	S	A	L	T
B	A	T		S	O	R	T	I	E	S
			A	N	A		N	A	B	

128

S	F	C	S			M	C	C	V	
E	L	A	L		B	A	R	C	A	
C	A	N	O	P	E	N	E	R	S	
T	I	T		A	L	E	A			
	R	A	N	E	E		M	E	D	E
		B	A	L	M	Y		D	A	D
A	H	I	L	L		A	M	I	S	S
C	E	L		A	I	M	A	T		
A	S	E	A		V	A	P	O	R	
		B	L	A	H		R	H	O	
	C	O	R	O	N	A	T	I	O	N
	A	D	A	M	S		K	A	N	E
	B	E	M	E		O	L	E	A	

Solutions

129

H	E	A	L	■		H	O	T	S	■
I	R	A	I	L	■	E	C	R	U	S
V	I	R	E	O	■	A	H	O	R	A
E	T	O	■	N	O	D	S	O	F	F
S	U	N	B	E	A	M	■	P	E	E
■	S	O	L	T	I	■	C	I	T	
I	M	P	L	Y		S	L	A	T	Y
N	A	E	■	H	I	T	O	R	■	
T	I	L	■	E	T	R	U	R	I	A
I	L	L	M	A	D	E	■	I	S	L
M	E	I	E	R	■	S	H	E	E	T
E	R	N	S	T	■	S	A	R	E	E
■	S	G	A	S	■	T	S	A	R	

130

A	I	D	S	■	A	F	F	E	C	T
F	O	A	L	■	S	A	T	R	A	P
A	N	T	A	■	T	V	S	E	T	S
R	E	S	T	O	R	E	■			
■			P	O	S	S	E	S	S	
S	T	A	T	U	S	■	G	A	T	O
H	O	R	A	S	■	H	A	T	E	A
E	L	E	C	■	S	U	S	A	N	S
S	L	O	T	C	A	R	■			
■			C	U	T	L	A	S	S	
M	O	D	E	L	T	■	A	R	C	H
A	R	R	I	V	E	■	R	I	A	A
D	I	E	S	I	S	■	A	S	M	Y

131

F	I	E	■	I	G	A	■	O	P	A
E	D	S	■	E	R	S	■	U	R	I
N	I	P	■	R	A	T	A	T	A	T
D	O	R	A	■	D	O	U	B	T	■
S	T	I	F	L	E	■	N	O	T	S
■		T	R	A	C	■	T	A	L	E
E	S	D	■	A	R	S	■	R	E	T
D	E	E	S	■	O	K	E	D	■	
D	A	C	E	■	S	I	G	M	A	S
■	L	O	A	F	S	■	S	O	M	E
A	I	R	M	A	I	L	■	T	A	G
T	O	P	■	I	N	A	■	O	R	A
A	N	S	■	L	G	S	■	R	E	L

132

C	A	P	S	■		C	U	R	E	
A	L	A	E	■	T	M	I	N	U	S
W	E	L	L	M	E	A	N	I	N	G
■	R	E	F	O	R	M	E	R	■	
■		R	U	N	A	M	O	K	■	
L	E	V	E	E	■	S	A	Y	I	N
A	N	E	S	■			T	A	L	I
B	U	S	T	S	■	R	O	L	L	E
■	F	I	R	E	B	U	G	■		
■	C	A	R	E	E	R	E	D	■	
D	E	L	I	B	E	R	A	T	E	D
O	P	E	N	O	N	■	P	U	G	S
B	A	S	T	■		H	I	S	S	

Solutions

133

```
B A M A . . E D A M E S
A G A S . F O R C E S .
B A R S . F U T I L E .
E L S . D E G S . . . .
. . U R I C H . W B A .
R E P A S T . B A R D .
U N I N H I B I T E D .
S O A K . V O W E L L .
E S L . S E G A R . . .
. . . T E N S . P G A .
S E D A T E . G O O D .
F R A C A S . A L I A .
C A N O E S . P O N Y .
```

134

```
B E E N . A G U E S . .
R N A S . B A R T E R .
A S S A S S I N A T E .
G U Y . P E N . M F A .
S E A M A N . I R V .
. . . C R T S . N E E .
A D D I S . A S E E D .
M I A . E C H O . . . .
P E C . D A Y L I T .
E C O . A R R . O S H .
R A I L R O A D T I E .
E S T E E M . I S A O .
. T Y R O S . A A H S .
```

135

```
O A F S . . C H A S .
T U R I N . A I L E D
I R E N E . I N T R A
T O E . A M S . E A N
I R T . L I S . R P G
S A H L . N O O N E S
. . R O S A N N A . .
I S O B A R . A T A D
D E W . D E A . I S E
E A L . N T H . V O A
A L I C E . A M E N D
L I N U S . B E L I E
. T E L S . D Y A N .
```

136

```
R E A C H . S L A S H
A L U L A . C A N N Y
D E T E R . R Y N E S
I C H . E D A . U R O
A T O . M A P . I T N
N O R M . S P A T .
T R I A D . Y U C C A
. T O E S . S O A P
B E A . P A C . E S A
R N R . R E L . P S T
A N I M E . A C T I I
S E A M S . S T I N T
H A N E S . S U S I E
```

Solutions

137

	A	M	C	S		M	A	D	D	
A	R	O	O	M		A	K	E	E	M
S	A	U	D	I	A	R	A	B	I	A
C	M	S		T	W	I		A	C	R
A	I	S		H	A	N	D	S	E	T
N	S	E	C		R	E	M	E	D	Y
			O	P	E	R	A			
S	N	A	P	O	N		J	A	N	A
T	E	N	T	P	E	G		L	E	R
A	R	I		P	S	U		E	S	L
C	O	M	M	I	S	E	R	A	T	E
K	L	U	T	E		S	A	S	E	S
	I	S	M	S		S	E	T	A	

138

S	O	A	K			S	C	A	B	S
E	N	G	E	L		A	T	R	I	P
T	E	R	R	E	S	T	R	I	A	L
T	E	E		E	P	I		A	L	A
L	A	E	R	T	E	S		N	Y	S
E	R	D	A		A	F	R	E	S	H
			T	O	K	Y	O			
C	A	S	T	L	E		T	E	T	S
R	B	I		D	A	Y	C	A	R	E
A	R	G		S	S	E		S	Y	N
V	A	N	I	T	Y	P	R	E	S	S
A	D	O	B	E		S	A	U	T	E
T	E	N	O	R			P	P	S	S

139

A	M	P	E	D			L	S	A	T
D	V	O	R	A	K		T	H	U	R
L	I	L	L	I	E		D	R	E	I
		Y	E	L	L	S		E	R	G
E	L	D		Y	S	T	A	D		
S	E	A	L		O	U	T	D	I	D
N	I	C	E	R		N	O	E	A	R
E	A	T	S	I	T		E	D	N	A
		Y	E	A	R	S		W	S	W
D	S	L		S	Y	N	T	H		
A	T	O	P		S	E	W	E	R	S
S	O	U	S		T	R	E	A	T	Y
H	A	S	T			T	E	T	E	S

140

M	A	C	E			O	M	E	A	R	A
A	B	A	S			F	A	R	M	E	R
T	A	U	S			F	R	A	C	A	S
			S	E	P	S	I	S			
		S	A	N	A		S	E	L	E	S
L	I	T	E	R			T	R	E	A	S
E	L	I							M	T	N
E	L	O	R	A		P	R	O	M	S	
S	Y	N	O	D		G	E	N	E		
			N	O	I	S	E	S			
C	A	N	A	R	D			S	O	R	T
A	N	G	L	E	E			E	L	E	A
W	O	O	D	E	D			S	E	C	T

Solutions

141

M	M	E			S	P	H			H	A	S
D	E	R			T	A	U			E	R	Y
A	I	R	T	E	R	M	I	N	A	L		
			T	R	E	M	O	R				
D	A	M	O	N	R	U	N	Y	O	N		
E	L	O	P	E			S	A	C	C	O	
C	I	D							L	O	W	
A	T	E	A	T		O	B	A	M	A		
L	O	R	D	S	P	R	A	Y	E	R		
		A	U	T	U	M	N					
I	N	T	E	R	R	O	G	A	T	E		
C	I	O		A	E	R			R	I	G	
E	E	R		P	E	E			M	N	O	

142

						A	M	E				
	M	A	E	N	A	D			R	K	O	
P	A	D	D	I	N	G			H	E	W	
T	A	V	I		S	E	R	I	A	L		
A	M	E	N	U			I	N	N	E		
S	S	N		P	A	S	S	O	U	T		
		T	W	O	S	T	E	P				
J	O	U	R	N	E	Y		L	L	D		
I	N	R	I		X	R	A	Y	S			
B	L	I	T	H	E		E	S	S	O		
E	A	S		A	R	I	S	T	O	S		
S	Y	M		D	A	C	T	Y	L			
				I	S	S						

143

B	A	B	S		S	L	A	C	K	S
A	N	E	T		R	O	L	L	I	E
S	I	E	R	R	A	L	E	O	N	E
S	P	R	E	E		A	G	E	D	
		S	A	L	E	S				
S	A	S	S		A	S	T	A	N	A
A	C	E		B	S	O		A	O	L
P	A	M	P	A	S		R	A	R	E
		E	N	O	L	A				
A	B	E	S			I	G	E	T	A
R	E	V	E	R	E	N	T	I	A	L
I	N	I	T	I	O		A	N	D	I
S	T	E	A	M	S		G	E	S	T

144

D	E	A	F	T	O			B	B	A
U	S	U	R	E	R			O	L	E	S
D	A	R	E	M	E			V	I	S	A
			E	P	I	L	E	P	S	Y
C	O	N	S	I	D	E	R			
A	N	E	W		A	D	A	G	I	O
V	I	V	I	D		A	C	O	R	N
A	N	E	M	I	A		H	O	M	O
		M	A	R	Z	I	P	A	N	
F	I	L	I	G	R	E	E			
A	N	I	N		E	L	V	E	R	S
S	O	N	G		A	D	E	S	T	E
O	R	A		R	A	R	E	S	T	

Solutions

145

S	T	E	M	S		W	I	L	D	
C	O	S	E	C		O	T	O	E	S
A	P	P	R	O	P	R	I	A	T	E
M	T	A		O	R	K		F	A	N
P	E	N	A	T	E	S		E	I	S
I	N	A	N		C	U	D	D	L	E
			T	R	I	P	E			
C	A	R	I	E	S		U	S	N	A
A	D	E		A	I	R	M	A	I	L
N	E	C		L	O	I		M	C	I
E	X	A	M	I	N	A	T	I	O	N
D	E	L	I	S		N	E	A	L	E
	C	L	A	M		T	A	M	E	S

146

S	C	A	D	S			U	R	B
C	A	M	E	T	O		A	B	E	E
U	S	E	N	E	T		M	A	T	S
T	A	B	U		C	O	B	N	U	T
U	L	A	N		S	I	G	N	O
M	S	E	C		R	E	V	I	E	W
			I	C	O	S	A		
C	O	B	A	L	T		L	E	A	D
A	N	O	T	E		E	N	D	O
S	E	N	I	O	R		N	S	E	C
I	S	N	O		A	T	T	E	S	T
N	E	I	N		G	E	L	A	T	O
O	T	E			T	Y	L	E	R

147

L	E	O	N	A		A	T	T	O	
A	V	O	I	D		N	E	U	R	O
B	E	L	L	Y	D	A	N	C	E	R
E	N	A		T	E	L		K	L	M
L	U	L	L	A	B	Y		I	S	E
	P	A	O		E	Z	I	N	E	
		A	C	N	E	S			
	A	S	N	O	T		U	L	E	
D	N	A		V	U	L	P	I	N	E
E	C	T		E	R	O		N	I	S
S	H	I	R	R	E	D	E	G	G	S
C	O	R	F	U		E	D	E	M	A
	R	E	S	P		S	T	R	A	Y

148

B	E	S	T		S	H	E	E	T	S
O	T	T	O		T	I	G	E	R	I
I	T	A	R		A	C	R	O	S	S
S	U	R	P	R	I	S	E		
		T	O	A	N		S	D	A	K
S	M	A	R	T	S		S	I	C	A
L	I	N						V	I	M
A	T	E	E		C	H	A	I	S	E
W	A	W	A		H	O	D	S		
			S	O	R	O	R	I	T	Y
D	I	N	E	R	O		I	B	O	S
M	I	R	I	A	M		F	L	O	E
D	I	A	N	N	E		T	E	T	R

Solutions

149

```
R A M I S █ P I C A S
O R A N T █ U N H I P
M A G D A █ S T I L T
O W N E R S H I P █ █
█ █ I N L A Y █ S E W
L O F T E D █ █ A N O
I I I █ T S E █ N C R
S L C █ █ A N A D E M
P Y A █ A C C T S █ █
█ █ T O O K A T A X I
S A I N T █ S E L M A
S P O D E █ E S S E N
A P N E A █ S T A N S
```

150

```
E D E S S A █ S R T A
D E A L E R █ Y E A R
S C R O D S █ S M I T
█ █ N E G █ P O S S E
R A I S E D U P █ █ █
I G N █ █ I N S E C T
M T G █ A O K █ X I I
A S S I G N █ █ P G A
█ █ R E S T L E S S █
M Y L E S █ B A D █ █
A E O N █ D O V I S H
E L L E █ O N E T W O
S P A S █ B E R E F T
```

151

```
C O R E S █ A F B S █
A L E N E █ M A R T A
R E A C T I O N A R Y
E A P █ F C C █ N E E
E T E █ R E O R D E R
R E D O E S █ O O P S
█ █ █ N E H R U █ █ █
E N N E █ E Y E L E T
L O O K S E E █ E M O
I S R █ O T B █ G O S
S I A M E S E C A T S
A D I E U █ E S T E E
█ E N T R █ R U E R S
```

152

```
P E D R O █ U N P E G
P R Y E R █ M O R T E
S I E G E █ P S E U D
█ █ D I O R █ T R I S
S A I S █ O T R A █ █
U S N █ S S H A P E D
B E T █ O E O █ H A I
S C H O L A R █ A S K
█ █ E D I T █ J E T E
D O W D █ E T A L █ █
A L O E S █ A L I T O
I L O S T █ S A T A Y
S A L T Y █ E P E E S
```

Solutions

153

U	M	A		R	E	P		C	B	S
S	A	T		U	R	L		H	A	W
A	M	M	O	N	I	A		E	N	E
		C	O	N	C	R	E	T	E	
R	O	W	A	N		K	A	P	U	T
O	V	E	R		R	E	V			
C	A	N	I	N	E	T	E	E	T	H
		N	O	T		N	E	A	R	
O	R	G	A	N		B	I	N	D	S
T	E	A	S	P	O	O	N			
H	E	M		L	U	G	G	A	G	E
E	V	E		U	S	E		C	O	G
R	E	D		S	T	Y		T	O	G

154

A	S	Y	O	U		M	E	R	C	
L	I	V	E	S		O	L	E	A	N
L	E	E	D	S		S	H	I	N	E
S	S	S		T	I	E	I	N	T	O
E	T	S		E	E	S		C	O	N
T	A	T	T	E	R		B	A	R	S
		L	O	L		P	E	R		
A	H	A	S		D	O	N	N	E	R
L	E	U		S	O	S		A	C	E
V	A	R	I	A	N	T		T	A	N
A	D	E	L	E		M	O	I	R	E
R	E	N	I	N		A	N	O	T	E
	R	T	E	S		N	E	N	E	S

155

	E	C	A	R	T	E		L	A	H
	F	I	S	H	E	S		I	P	A
	F	R	E	E	A	G	E	N	T	S
S	A	R	E	E	S		A	G	E	S
S	C	U	D		K	R	U	S	H	
T	E	S		N	E	O	N	A	T	E
		T	E	N	K	S				
L	U	M	B	A	G	O		B	I	L
A	B	O	I	L		D	A	C	E	
S	O	U	R		G	O	R	G	E	S
H	A	N	D	I	N	H	A	N	D	
E	T	D		T	A	E	N	I	A	
D	S	S		D	R	D	O	O	M	

156

A	L	A		M	T	M		L	E	G
C	O	S		C	O	E		E	L	A
M	A	S	C	A	R	A		A	I	S
E	N	T	O		S	T	A	K	E	S
		A	H	O	Y	S				
T	I	L	L	I	S		S	A	D	A
S	L	E	E	P		N	A	M	E	S
O	L	E	S		S	E	S	A	M	E
		C	E	T	U	S				
A	P	P	E	A	R		I	M	O	N
D	A	R		T	O	R	N	A	D	O
O	R	O		I	B	E		M	E	R
G	A	D		T	E	A		A	A	M

Solutions

157

```
A P R S   E G I S E S
B A H T   N O N P R O
A S Y E   V E R I T Y
A S T R   I R E N E S
    H E A R S
K I M O N O     V W S
I N I   O N T   I O N
A F C   M A R V E L
      M E D I A
T R I T O N   C C U P
R E B O O T   H I L O
A B O L L A   I T E N
C A S U A L   E Y E D
```

158

```
P I L E S     A M F M
A C E L A   P A Y E E
N O M A D   A S S E T
I N O   A T T   T B A
N I N   T H E C E L L
I C A L   E N U R E S
    D Y N A S T Y
S E E O U T   E N S E
E N S N A R E   O T S
M D T   N E T   V E T
I S A A C   A B E L E
T I N G E   P A L M E
E T D S     E P S O M
```

159

```
E M B E D   E D E M A
E A R L E   M A N E T
G R E A T C I R C L E
S E R S   O L E S O N
      T O N Y S
R O S I N S   P R E
E J E C T O R S E A T
A S A   N E A R T O
    K I A N G
A T D A W N   E D N A
R E S T I T U T I O N
I N O I L   G E N R E
A N S E L   O A S I S
```

160

```
L U C C I     A D I A
A V A U N T   S O D A
W A R S A W   H I S S
    O P P O S E
N U L   I S P   H I C
O R I N G   A G E N A
B A N N S   R O N A S
I N A W E   E A R L E
D O S   Y E T   I L S
    R E C I T E
A S I S   O R A T O R
G A M S   L E S T E R
S O A S   S E A N S
```

Solutions

161

P	A	B	S	T		S	H	R	E	D
O	L	L	I	E		H	E	I	D	I
W	A	T	E	R	C	A	N	N	O	N
S	D	S		R	O	M		G	M	A
			M	I	X	U	P	S		
N	E	S	T	E	A		T	I	E	D
A	S	T	I	R		C	E	D	A	R
G	A	E	D		C	A	R	E	S	S
		M	Y	H	E	R	O			
S	P	A		O	R	D		T	A	B
P	O	R	T	R	A	I	T	U	R	E
E	R	I	E	S		A	W	M	A	N
S	E	E	M	E		C	O	S	T	S

162

A	S	W	E		I	R	K	E	D	
D	O	O	M		R	O	N	A	S	
F	I	L	T	E	R	T	I	P	S	
E	L	F		G	U	L	F			
E	S	H	A	R	P		E	B	A	Y
		O	N	E	T	O		I	B	O
R	O	U	E	S		H	O	P	O	N
O	L	N		S	T	E	L	A		
H	A	D	I		E	N	E	R	G	Y
			T	E	T	R		T	E	E
	D	E	A	D	L	Y	S	I	N	S
O	L	L	I	E			O	T	R	O
T	A	S	T	Y		G	E	E	R	

163

F	I	C	A				A	M	A	T
E	C	O	N	O		L	L	A	M	A
E	E	N	S	Y		A	P	R	I	L
D	E	F		S	A	G	E	S		
		E	R	T	E	S		N	I	C
L	A	D	I	E	S		C	E	C	E
A	R	E	A	R		W	O	E	B	E
L	I	R	A		M	A	N	D	M	S
A	L	A		J	I	B	E	S		
		T	H	E	D	A		M	E	D
A	D	I	O	S		S	H	O	R	E
R	O	O	S	T		H	E	M	E	N
A	N	N	S				A	S	S	T

164

T	A	K	A		R	A	G	M	O	P
I	K	E	S		O	B	L	A	T	E
A	I	M	S		N	E	U	R	O	N
	O	P	I	O	N	E	E	R	S	
			S	P	I	R	O			
D	E	V	I	S	E		N	Y	R	O
B	C	C						U	P	S
A	G	R	A		O	K	A	P	I	S
			L	E	N	I	N			
	C	O	M	P	A	N	I	O	N	
D	O	L	O	O	P		T	H	O	M
O	L	I	N	D	A		R	E	L	Y
M	A	D	D	E	R		A	R	L	O

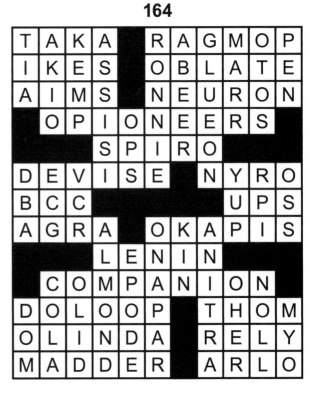

Solutions

165

	S	M	I	R	K				A	B	A
S	E	A	N	C	E			S	S	R	S
T	A	R	T	A	R			U	S	I	N
E	L	S	E			R	E	P	U	T	E
L	E	H	R			S	E	R	O	W	
A	R	A	M		S	O	R	E	N		
			I	T	A	L	S				
	A	P	S	I	S			T	U	B	A
O	B	E	S	E				I	N	A	N
F	A	C	I	A	L		T	E	T	E	
A	S	T	O		O	P	I	A	T	E	
G	E	I	N		C	L	O	S	E	D	
E	R	N			H	O	N	E	R		

166

S	A	C			I	K	O			C	A	D
A	D	O			N	I	C			O	T	E
M	O	N			U	N	A			M	R	I
O	R	S			R	E	N	A	M	E	S	
S	E	C	R	E	T	A	R	I	A	T		
A	D	I	A			I	D	E	S	T		
			O	I	L	C	A	N	S			
	M	U	S	E	E			D	I	D	A	
C	O	S	I	G	N	A	T	O	R	Y		
R	U	N	N	I	E	R			N	I	E	
A	S	E			B	R	I			E	P	S
C	S	S			L	G	S			R	P	I
K	E	S			E	Y	E			S	Y	R

167

R	I	C	E	R			M	R	A	N	D
E	G	A	L	E			E	A	T	O	N
V	O	L	K	S	W	A	G	E	N	S	
S	O	C		E	I	N	E				
	N	U	D	E	S	T		T	H	I	
		L	I	K	E	A	S	H	O	T	
O	N	A	S			W	E	R	E		
O	N	T	H	E	B	E	A	M			
F	E	E		T	I	L	T	A	T		
		O	H	N	O		S	E	N		
C	U	T	A	N	D	P	A	S	T	E	
I	M	A	R	I		E	V	E	R	I	
E	P	I	S	C		S	I	S	A	L	

168

H	A	R	P	O			M	A	D	A	M
A	T	E	A	R			I	T	I	N	A
R	O	A	R	K			S	T	R	A	T
D	E	L	T	A	B	L	U	E	S		
			D	E	N	S	E				
A	G	E	R		S	A	U	C	E	R	
P	E	A	R	L		D	L	I	S	T	
A	S	L	E	E	P		T	N	T	S	
			T	A	K	E	N				
	A	L	L	T	H	E	R	A	G	E	
A	R	O	S	E		A	I	M	E	E	
R	A	D	A	R		N	O	O	N	E	
E	M	I	T	S		E	R	N	E	S	

Solutions

169

S	P	A	C	E	D				E	O	S
L	A	C	O	N	I	C			E	O	S
U	N	C	L	E	A	R			N	N	E
E	D	O			L	O	N	G	E	R	
D	A	M	N	S			C	E	I	B	A
	S	P	A	I	N			S	N	C	C
		L	U	N	E	T	T	E			
O	T	I	S			W	O	L	D	S	
W	I	S	E	S			P	E	R	C	H
I	N	H	A	L	E			I	R	A	
N	E	E			A	R	R	I	V	A	L
G	A	D			P	R	E	C	E	P	T
					S	T	E	R	E	S	

170

A	S	C	H			A	R	I	S	T	A
L	O	A	D			S	H	E	A	R	S
D	A	N	L			S	E	R	G	E	I
A	P	I		B	E	T			E	E	N
		S	C	O	T	T	S				
A	N	T	O	N	S			T	O	B	E
D	E	E	R	E			S	O	N	A	R
E	A	R	P		C	L	I	C	H	E	
		S	C	A	R	C	E				
N	I	L		O	T	S		M	D	A	
A	R	C	T	O	S			B	O	R	G
S	U	D	O	K	U			B	R	E	E
I	N	S	T	E	P			S	E	I	S

171

R	I	M		A	K	A			S	F	C
S	C	O	R	N	E	D			A	L	L
S	Y	N	O	N	Y	M			D	U	I
		I	T	I	S	I			H	M	O
O	U	T	I	E			R	E	U	P	S
S	R	O			M	E	L				
F	O	R	E	V	E	R	M	O	R	E	
			W	I	E			N	B	A	
C	R	E	W	S			T	I	E	I	N
R	E	S		T	I	A	G	O			
E	D	S		U	N	L	O	C	K	S	
S	I	E		L	A	C	T	A	I	D	
C	D	X		A	S	S			T	P	S

172

B	A	S	T			L	A	C	A	S	A
A	S	T	A			I	S	O	M	E	R
S	E	A	U			S	T	N	I	C	K
I	A	T		O	P	E	C				
S	T	I	E	B			R	O	P	E	D
			O	X	O			N	U	E	V	E
C	A	N	T				R	T	E	S	
M	Y	E	R	S			A	S	T		
D	E	R	A	T			W	E	I	S	S
			D	O	C	E			C	T	A
P	A	T	I	N	A			P	O	O	L
E	L	A	T	E	S			A	A	R	E
S	E	C	E	D	E			S	T	E	S

Solutions

173

A	C	A	I			O	P	E	R	A
S	A	N	S		F	L	O	R	A	L
A	N	A	S		I	N	S	A	N	E
S	I	T	U	P	S		T	S	K	S
		H	E	E	H	E	E			
E	D	E		N	E	A	R	E	S	T
G	A	M		N	Y	T		M	E	I
G	O	A	T	E	E	S		I	S	O
		A	D	L	I	B	S			
S	P	A	R		E	N	E	S	C	O
P	I	G	P	E	N		L	I	E	D
F	L	O	O	R	S		L	O	R	D
S	E	N	N	A			I	N	E	S

174

S	H	I	R	R		B	E	S	E	T
T	O	N	I	O		O	K	E	M	O
A	L	A	N	S		T	E	N	E	T
N	E	P		E	L	O		I	R	A
E	S	P		B	O	X		O	I	L
	R	E	U	P		E	R	T	E	
S	T	E	E	D		B	E	M	A	D
P	E	C	K		A	E	R	O		
U	N	I		A	A	A		M	O	S
T	S	A		B	E	T		E	S	T
T	I	B	I	A		S	A	N	T	E
E	L	L	I	S		I	N	T	E	R
R	E	E	S	E		T	Y	S	O	N

175

S	L	A	T		A	M	R	I	T	A
L	A	M	A		S	E	A	L	I	N
A	L	E	K		T	I	T	L	E	D
P	A	R	A	K	E	E	T			
		A	R	R	E	A	R	S		
N	I	S	S	A	N		D	R	I	P
O	C	T	E	T		K	O	A	L	A
M	E	A	L		Y	E	N	N	E	D
S	T	R	A	P	I	N				
		S	E	E	S	P	A	S	T	
T	E	A	S	E	L		A	B	I	E
R	E	M	I	N	D		S	A	P	S
A	S	S	E	S	S		S	A	S	S

176

I	D	S		G	M	A				
N	O	U		S	I	N		V	E	T
A	P	P	R	O	X	I	M	A	T	E
W	E	R	E		E	L	I	N	O	R
E	Y	E	L	I	D		S	T	I	R
	M	O	A	B		S	A	L	E	
W	E	E		M	L	S		G	E	T
A	L	B	A		E	T	R	E		
S	E	E	P		S	L	I	P	B	Y
A	V	I	S	O	S		S	O	R	A
B	E	N	E	D	I	C	T	I	O	N
I	N	G		E	N	A		N	O	N
		S	G	T		T	M	I		

Solutions

177

	F	D	I	C			I	J	K	L	
P	L	E	B	E			Q	U	E	E	R
H	A	M	A	L			S	T	E	N	O	
A	G	A	R	I	C			S	P	O	T	
S	O	N			A	A	S			S	R	O
E	N	D	S			D	E	N	I	E	R
		A	T	L	E	A	S	T			
J	E	R	K	I	N			F	I	F	A
O	D	E			L	C	D			N	I	N
K	I	W	I			E	D	A	M	E	S
E	T	A	T	S			A	R	I	S	E
D	O	R	S	A			Y	E	N	T	L
	R	D	A	S			S	O	D	A	

178

C	H	A	S	E			C	O	A	T	I
H	O	V	E	L			O	R	R	I	N
O	N	E	R	S			R	E	I	G	N
W	E	S	T	E	R	N	I	Z	E		
			A	S	E	E	D			
C	A	P	S			L	A	A	L	A	A
A	A	M						E	R	A
F	A	S	T	E	N			C	A	N	E
		O	L	A	F	S				
	A	C	R	O	B	A	T	I	C	S
A	T	A	R	I			B	O	X	U	P
M	A	T	E	S			E	R	I	S	A
A	N	O	S	E			R	E	A	P	S

179

	H	I	L	L			U	L	N	A	
M	A	N	I	A			N	O	E	N	D
A	C	T	A	S			F	A	C	T	O
I	K	E			S	U	R	F	E	I	T
T	S	R			O	S	O			S	S	E
A	A	R	E			A	C	I	S		
I	W	O	N	T			K	R	A	A	L
		G	E	R	E			E	R	M	A
T	U	A			O	T	C			Y	S	L
I	N	T	R	U	S	T			E	T	A
S	C	I	O	N			R	A	V	E	L
H	A	V	O	C			L	A	I	L	A
	P	E	T	E			S	A	L	S	

180

H	E	B	R	E	W			N	D	A	K
O	R	I	O	L	E			F	I	L	E
R	E	P	O	S	S	E	S	S	E	D	
			M	E	T	Z		R	A	S	
B	R	A	S	S	E	R	I	E			
A	E	F			R	A	N	G	E	D	
N	A	T	I	O	N	S	T	A	T	E	
S	M	E	L	L	S				R	A	M
		R	E	L	A	T	E	D	T	O	
B	E	D			I	H	O	P			
O	N	E	Y	E	A	R	O	L	D	S	
O	N	C	E			R	A	C	I	N	E
S	A	K	S			A	S	H	C	A	N

Solutions

181

D	U	C	A	T		O	H	A	R	A
O	M	A	R	A		S	O	L	A	R
C	A	R	O	N		H	O	O	H	A
		D	O	T	H		L	U	S	T
C	O	G		E	Q	U	I			
A	B	A	B		S	A	G	E	L	Y
T	I	M	I	D		R	A	L	E	S
S	E	E	R	E	D		N	E	N	E
		D	E	E	T		C	A	R	
A	S	P	S		G	A	T	T		
C	O	O	E	R		S	E	I	S	M
C	A	L	E	B		T	R	O	O	P
S	K	E	D	S		E	N	N	I	S

182

O	F	T		T	R	O	W	E	L
L	O	E	B		I	N	T	E	N	T
E	R	L	E		M	A	T	T	E	D
S	T	E	E	L	E					
	M	O	N	I	C	A		S	K	A
T	Y	L	E	N	O	L		T	I	N
R	E	O		G	N	U		O	N	A
A	R	G		O	S	M	O	N	D	S
P	S	Y		S	U	N	D	E	W	
			M	A	I	D	O	F		
W	A	P	I	T	I		S	E	R	I
O	P	E	R	O	N		T	A	D	A
P	E	N	A	N	G		D	S	T	

183

C	S	U		T	A	G		S	A	B
O	L	N		A	B	O		O	A	R
L	O	W	P	R	E	S	S	U	R	E
D	E	A	R	S		P	A	L	E	D
	R	O	E		E	F	S			
P	A	R	C	S		L	E	E	C	H
A	F	A	R		T	A	R	T		
P	I	N	E	S		L	Y	R	I	C
	T	A	H		E	N	C			
S	L	A	T	E		M	E	H	T	A
H	I	B	E	R	N	A	T	I	O	N
A	L	L		E	O	N		N	I	N
W	Y	E		E	S	S		G	T	E

184

B	R	E	E	D		R	A	T	S	O
S	A	V	E	R		O	D	I	U	M
S	P	A	R	E	C	H	A	N	G	E
		I	D	I		M	O	E	N	
G	L	E	E		G	P	A			
A	I	T		M	A	I	N	M	A	N
L	E	I	S	U	R	E	T	I	M	E
E	N	C	O	D	E	R		N	Y	U
		I	S	T		A	S	S	N	
A	L	O	G		T	S	U			
L	I	O	N	H	E	A	R	T	E	D
I	N	R	E	D		M	A	R	I	S
A	N	T	E	S		S	E	U	S	S

Solutions

185

B	A	I	R	D	■	S	C	A	M	P
A	L	T	E	R	■	T	A	M	A	R
D	I	S	A	S	S	E	M	B	L	E
D	A	I	S	■	T	A	E	■	■	■
■	■	S	E	A	L	■	C	C	I	■
S	E	T	U	P	S	■	A	F	A	R
H	E	A	R	T	H	S	T	O	N	E
A	R	N	E	■	A	B	A	S	E	D
D	O	A	■	S	W	A	P	■	■	■
■	■	E	P	A	■	R	A	G	S	■
F	A	M	I	L	Y	B	I	B	L	E
I	R	A	N	I	■	O	C	E	A	N
B	E	A	S	T	■	N	E	E	D	S

186

M	C	A	T	■	L	A	R	E	D	O
Y	U	L	E	■	I	R	E	N	E	S
G	O	L	D	E	N	R	I	N	G	S
O	M	A	■	L	E	A	■	O	R	U
D	O	N	O	V	A	N	■	B	E	A
■	■	■	O	I	L	■	N	L	E	R
M	O	R	N	S	■	P	O	E	S	Y
A	N	O	A	■	B	I	T	■	■	■
D	A	M	■	T	O	N	I	E	S	T
E	D	A	■	A	T	O	■	T	A	O
P	A	N	I	C	A	T	T	A	C	K
A	R	I	S	E	N	■	A	I	R	Y
R	E	A	L	T	Y	■	C	L	E	O

187

R	A	F	T	E	R	■	■	D	A	T
A	L	B	E	D	O	■	P	I	C	A
W	E	I	R	D	O	■	R	E	A	L
■	■	■	C	O	S	M	E	T	I	C
O	G	L	E	■	T	O	E	■	■	■
D	A	U	N	T	■	O	X	B	O	W
D	I	T	T	O	■	S	I	E	G	E
S	T	E	E	P	■	E	S	T	E	R
■	■	N	A	N	■	T	H	E	E	■
M	A	G	A	Z	I	N	E	■	■	■
U	S	E	R	■	T	E	N	D	E	R
T	I	N	Y	■	R	A	C	E	M	E
T	A	T	■	O	P	E	N	U	P	■

188

S	H	E	■	D	A	B	■	T	R	I
O	E	N	■	E	M	O	■	E	E	N
C	A	V	I	T	Y	W	A	L	L	S
I	T	O	N	■	L	E	S	L	E	Y
O	H	I	O	U	■	S	I	A	N	■
■	■	U	S	A	R	■	N	S	C	■
■	P	A	R	T	R	I	D	G	E	■
A	L	L	■	A	C	T	H	■	■	■
L	A	C	E	■	■	T	A	E	B	O
A	T	O	N	C	E	■	B	L	E	T
M	O	H	A	W	K	R	I	V	E	R
O	O	O	■	T	E	M	■	E	C	O
S	N	L	■	S	D	S	■	S	H	S

Solutions

189

C	A	D	D	Y	■	A	U	R	A	L
O	P	E	R	A	■	I	N	O	N	E
M	O	R	O	N	■	M	D	C	C	I
B	L	A	N	K	V	E	R	S	E	■
■	O	N	E	S	I	D	E	■	■	■
E	G	G	■	■	L	A	S	S	I	E
L	I	E	G	E	■	T	S	A	D	E
M	A	D	A	S	A	■	V	A	N	
■	■	S	T	A	L	K	E	R		
■	L	O	T	U	S	E	A	T	E	R
B	E	R	R	A	■	O	R	I	Y	A
O	N	A	I	R	■	R	A	M	O	S
N	A	N	C	Y	■	A	T	E	U	P

190

B	O	G	S	■	P	U	M	I	C	E
R	A	R	E	■	A	Z	A	R	I	A
I	T	E	S	■	C	I	T	R	O	N
C	H	A	S	T	I	S	E	■		
■	T	I	O	N	■	Y	E	T	I	
A	P	R	O	P	O	S	■	N	E	D
I	R	A	N	I	■	E	T	U	D	E
T	I	C	■	C	L	E	A	N	S	E
S	E	E	A	■	L	I	N	C	■	
■	N	O	O	N	T	I	M	E		
P	A	S	S	B	Y	■	R	A	E	S
A	T	W	O	O	D	■	U	T	N	E
P	L	A	N	E	S	■	M	E	A	S

191

U	M	M	A	■	O	I	L	I	L	Y
S	O	O	N	■	C	R	O	S	S	E
M	A	R	A	T	H	O	N	M	A	N
A	I	O	L	I	■	C	I	S	T	S
■	■	Y	N	E	Z	■				
A	M	A	Z	E	S	■	T	I	T	O
H	I	D	E	A	N	D	S	E	E	K
S	C	A	R	■	E	N	U	R	E	D
■	■	A	S	A	N	■				
S	H	A	R	P	■	S	A	M	O	A
M	I	S	S	T	H	E	M	A	R	K
E	R	E	S	T	U	■	I	N	N	O
W	E	S	S	O	N	■	S	E	E	N

192

L	A	S	C	A	L	A	■	D	N	S
E	C	U	A	D	O	R	■	E	O	N
T	H	E	K	I	N	G	A	N	D	I
T	I	B	E	T	■	O	W	N	U	P
E	E	E	S	■	S	N	A	I	L	S
D	R	E	■	C	O	A	R	S	E	■
■	■	S	A	L	U	D	■			
■	S	E	C	R	E	T	■	M	F	D
G	E	N	R	E	S	■	H	A	L	E
A	V	A	I	L	■	M	I	N	O	T
T	E	M	P	E	R	A	T	U	R	E
O	R	E	■	S	E	N	O	R	E	S
S	E	L	■	S	E	N	N	E	T	T

Solutions

193

```
S H I A █ T I S H R I
T E N N █ E R N E S T
R E C D █ D A I N T Y
O D O N █ D E P █ █ █
█ █ M O B Y █ P O E M
S A E █ A S S E N T S
A R T U R █ S T T N G
D E A L I N G █ H A R
R O X Y █ O T H E █ █
█ █ █ S E V █ O N E A
A G A S S I █ T O T S
E T C E T C █ S S T S
F O S S A E █ Y E A N
```

194

```
L O G E █ █ C A R O L
O I L U P █ A M E N D
A D O S E █ S T A E L
█ B E N C H █ D L S █
T H A █ A T I M E █ █
R O L L █ S E A M U S
I D I O M █ R I A T A
B A Z A A R █ O N E G
█ A M E B A █ D S O █
E C T █ S H R E W █ █
R A I T T █ E P E E S
A R O A R █ A P E R S
S A N Y O █ █ S P O T
```

195

```
S A T I T █ █ A L T I
O D E S A █ O N E A D
F R E A K Y D E A K Y
T I N █ E O E █ V I L
E V E █ I G N █ E N L
N E R D █ U S I N G █
█ █ █ E A R E D █ █ █
█ K E M P T █ A S P S
H A B █ A C H █ T U A
O H O █ T U B █ I T S
F L A S H P O I N T S
F I T L Y █ M C G E E
A L S O █ █ B U S E D
```

196

```
R P I █ C R U █ █ █
I E D █ E H S █ U A R
S L I P P E D I N T O
E L O I S E █ I P A D
R E S P █ A S A L E
S T Y P T I C █ R E O
█ N A U T I C A █ █
S L C █ C E D I L L A
H U R O K █ █ E L A L
R I A S █ S T R E A K
E S S E N T I A L L Y
D A Y █ O E N █ E A N
█ █ █ D R E █ D A E
```

Solutions

197

P	A	P	P		H	A	R	O	L	D
E	L	E	E		A	R	A	B	I	A
C	O	R	R	E	L	A	T	I	V	E
S	E	M	I	N	A	R				
		M	O	L	A	S	S	E	S	
C	U	K	E	S		T	E	E	N	A
A	N	A	T			M	A	I	L	
L	E	T	E	M		R	A	N	D	S
E	S	T	R	O	G	E	N			
		N	O	S	T	R	I	L		
P	L	A	Y	E	R	P	I	A	N	O
A	E	R	A	T	E		C	M	D	R
C	A	F	T	A	N		S	A	S	E

198

M	I	S	S	M		L	O	T	S	A
I	R	A	N	I		A	M	A	T	I
M	A	Y	O	R		S	O	B	E	R
I	B	E		A	B	S	O	L	V	E
C	U	R	A	C	A	O		E	E	R
		S	L	R		J	A	N	S	
	B	E	S	E	R	I	O	U	S	
S	E	A	N		A	S	I			
T	A	R		A	G	O	N	I	Z	E
I	G	N	O	B	E	L		F	A	V
G	L	E	N	N		A	M	I	G	A
M	E	S	N	E		T	O	D	A	D
A	S	T	O	R		E	M	O	T	E

199

A	R	A	N		S	I	L	A	N	E
B	A	L	E		I	S	A	D	O	R
L	I	M	O		S	E	A	A	I	R
E	M	A	N	A	T	E				
D	I	M		P	E	A	T	B	O	G
		A	M	O	R		A	R	N	E
A	C	T	A	S		S	L	A	T	E
T	I	E	R		P	I	C	S		
F	I	R	E	S	A	T		S	P	F
		C	R	U	C	I	A	L		
A	S	M	A	R	A		L	E	N	A
D	U	L	L	E	D		E	R	A	T
L	E	S	S	E	E		F	E	M	S

200

C	H	I	C				I	R	I	S
G	E	N	O	A		E	R	E	C	T
I	N	V	A	R		R	A	D	I	O
	E	X	C	H	E	Q	U	E	R	
S	O	S		H	O	B		C	R	Y
I	O	T	A		T	U	P	I		
C	H	I	N	A		S	I	N	C	E
		G	I	S	T		E	G	A	D
A	L	A		S	A	T		A	D	O
J	I	T	T	E	R	B	U	G		
U	N	I	A	T		S	K	E	A	N
G	A	O	L	S		P	E	N	C	E
A	C	N	E				S	T	E	W

Solutions

201

R	U	F	U	S		S	O	C	A	L
U	N	R	E	P		A	R	O	S	E
N	E	A	L	E		M	U	L	A	N
		N	E	C	C	O		L	Y	S
M	L	K		I	T	S	M	E		
E	I	L	E	E	N		A	C	R	O
S	E	A	L	S		C	A	T	I	E
H	U	N	S		C	A	S	E	I	N
		G	A	T	O	S		D	S	O
A	L	E		A	W	A	R	D		
N	I	L	E	S		B	O	A	S	T
E	L	L	E	S		A	M	T	O	O
S	T	A	L	E		S	A	A	B	S